CHURCH AND STATE

by

Dave Sim

Aardvark-Vanaheim Inc.
First printing, June 1987
Second printing, September 1989
Third printing, February 1992
Fourth printing, November 1992

ISBN 0-919359-09-4

Printed in Windsor, Ontario by
Preney Print & Litho Inc.

PRINTED IN CANADA

to Deni for her timely departure

to Gerhard for his timely arrival

and

to Jessica because somewhere it is
always January 23, 1984

CONTENTS

Book One
Aprés State

Book Two
Back to Iest

Book Three
Church and State

What you hold in your hands is the first half of a work-in-progress--that, as I write this, is a year and half away from completion. It is also the third part of a larger work-in-progress that, as I write this, is fifteen years and some months from completion. This volume has a cliffhanger ending. If you are the sort who is deeply offended by reading close to six-hundred pages that do not resolve themselves in a happily-ever-after, I would encourage you to put this book on a shelf out of your reach and wait (patiently or otherwise) for volume two which should see print sometime in 1989. Trust me. I'm dancing as fast as I can.

For those who purchased the previous volume **High Society,** the fictional city-state of Iest and many of the characters in **Church and State** will be familiar. Much of the religious background, settings and texts has been woven in ridiculous detail in my notebooks as this story evolved in Cerebus' monthly comic series. What has made it to the finished pages is a fraction of the resources created. Enough has been used to lend authenticity to the fiction. Enough has been left out to keep the story from reading like a term paper.

In much the same way that **High Society** reflected my genuine affection for the realities of political campaigning, elections and government, **Church and State** reflects a genuine affection for and interest in the effect of power on belief and vice versa. Those who find my observations to be distorted or insulting are encouraged to read any decent history of the papacy in the middle ages or watch reruns of Jim and Tammy. (I miss them already).

Dave Sim
April 26, 1987
Kitchener, Ontario

BOOK ONE
Aprés State

"On Governing"
by
Cerebus, Former Prime
Minister of Iest

Governing a city-state in today's world is very very difficult. There are many problems.

It is hoped that my own experiences as a leader will help to guide future leaders.

The first thing you have to do is ignore Lord Julius. Listening to him can cause you to lose up to Ten Thousand crowns _a day_. _No Joke!!_

The second thing is to invade only really rich countries and not listen to Lord Julius when he tells you which ones are rich.

14

The third thing is to fire all your advisors, once a week so they don't drive you _crazy_!!

SO HIS FRIEND RUSHES UP AND HE'S SCREAMING Y'KNOW -- ? ....

The fourth thing is to sell everything that isn't nailed down to hire armies. Fire any advisor who says you can't do this...

"YEW HEV NO _RIGHT_!!"

"YEW HEV NO _RIGHT_!!"

Eat only expensive food and drink only expensive liquor. It's the only good thing about being a leader.

SO I SWINGS MY SWORD AGAIN

WHACK!!

AN' I SAY "AT'S OKAY" HUH-HUH-HUH "YOU GOT NO _HEAD_!!"

Don't attend meetings and fire advisors who tell you you have to. All you do is sit there for hours while a bunch of whiners tell you what's wrong and you can't go to the bathroom.

SO I'M LAUGHIN' _SEE_ 'COS THE ONE GUY'S HEAD LANDS ON THE OTHER GUY'S ARM...

LIKE HE'S GIVIN' 'IM A _HUG_...

The only other good thing about being a leader is _quitting_... everyone who bugged you all the time is unemployed or under arrest. Ha-Ha. It looks good on them, too!!

SUDDENLY, I FEEL THIS SHARP PAIN IN MY _RIBS_...

I FIGGER I MUST HAVE BUST A GUT FOR _REAL_ LAUGHIN' SO HARD...

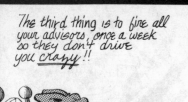

15

"On Governing"
by
Former Prime Minister Cerebus of Iest
PART the SECOND

The biggest thing you have to do is stop listening to people, except when they are telling you facts. As soon as they start saying opinions, you should stop listening. They always tell you that what you decided isn't going to be popular and then they ask you if you want to change your mind. I used to change my mind all the time when they said this, but then Cerebus started thinking; Why don't they just do what they're told? They wanted someone to make decisions, so they have an election, okay? Okay. It's like five guys out in the woods. And three of them say "So-and-so will be the leader." Okay? Okay. Now you've settled it. When so-and-so says "As leader, I think we should go this way" you don't stop and argue. That's why you made him leader. Cerebus thinks that after you vote, you should shut up and do as you're told or go to jail. Period. Otherwise nothing gets done.

Be careful, too, about farting around your butler. You shouldn't fart around anyone, really, because they start stammering and stuttering and you never find out what they were going to say and if you yell at them for stammering, they wet their pants. But especially not your butler, because if you fart when he's bringing you your soup, he spills it all over you.

the Insecure Sinecure

"AH! CEREBUS!" CRIES YOUNG LORD SILVERSPOON "WE HAVE FOUND A FRIENDLY FACE AT LAST...."

"AFTER YOU, MY GOOD FRIEND" MURMURS LORD TRYSTRIM, "YOUR OBEDIENT SERVANT" SAYS LORD GWANE "CLOVIS' PERFUME AND POWDER PUFF" MUTTERS THE EARTH-PIG BORN.

"I HAVE HAD MY EMPLOYMENT TERMINATED" HONKS THE YOUNG SNOB, ADDING, LACONICALLY "IF YOU CAN IMAGINE SUCH A THING."

"FIFTY CROWNS AND AN EVICTION NOTICE" HE WHINES. "IT IS AN OUTRAGE AGAINST MY MARKET VALUE AS AN OFFICIAL EMBARRASSMENT TO MY FATHER'S ADMINISTRATION."
"OFFICIAL EMBARRASSMENT?" QUERIES THE AARDVARK.

"DID I NOT TOAST THE PIRATES WHO HAVE BEEN DECIMATING MY FATHER'S SHIPPING FLEET?" POUTS THE YOUNG ARISTOCRAT. "DID I NOT WRITE LETTERS CONDEMNING PALNU'S EXPANSIONIST POLICIES?"

"INDEED, YOU DID," AGREES TRYSTRIM.

"YOU DID INDEED," CONCURS GWANE

"I EVEN TOLD THE STORY OF HOW LORD JULIUS SHOT HIMSELF IN THE FOOT WHILE LEARNING HOW TO FIRE A CROSSBOW," HE SIGHS. "THEY JUST DIDN'T REALIZE MY VALUE."

"THAT'LL BE SIX BITS," INTERRUPTS THE WAITER.

"I SEEM TO HAVE MISPLACED MY PURSE" INTERJECTS TRYSTRIM,

THE EARTH-PIG BITES HIS TONGUE.

"WHAT DID I DO WITH THAT HALF-CROWN?" FUMES GWANE.

"HERE," ANSWERS SILVERSPOON, "TAKE THIS AND GET OUT OF MY SIGHT UNTIL WE NEED MORE ALE."

"WHY -- THANK YOU, M'LORD," STAMMERS THE WAITER.

"THIS MUG IS FILTHY" SNORTS TRYSTRIM.

"THIS ALE IS WATERY," WHINES GWANE.

"I THINK IT IS TIME TO WRITE A LETTER" MUSES SILVERSPOON.

"PAPER AND INK" DEMANDS TRYSTRIM, SNAPPING HIS FINGERS.

"PAPER AND INK" ECHOES GWANE WITH MILITARY PRECISION.

"AND A PEN AS WELL" ADDS TRYSTRIM.

"A--UH--PEN" REITERATES GWANE UNCERTAINLY AS HE SEARCHES HIS POCKETS.

"MY DEAR COUNTESS DETIN COMMA" HE DICTATES," HAVING HEARD ABOUT MY FATHER'S REFUSAL TO DEFER TAXATION ON YOUR HOLDINGS IN PALNU COMMA I AM MOVED TO OFFER MY SERVICES PERIOD I WOULD REQUIRE ONLY FOOD AND SHELTER FOR MYSELF AND TWO COMPANIONS PARENTHESIS WHO WILL AID ME IN SEEKING JUSTICE FOR YOU PARENTHESIS PERIOD"

"PEN--TWO CROWNS" SUGGESTS CEREBUS GREEDILY.

"SOLD," ANNOUNCES SILVERSPOON.

"I SAY-- HOW WOULD YOU LIKE A NICE REST IN THE COUNTRY WHILE YOU WORK ON YOUR MEMOIRS" ASKS SILVERSPOON.

"MY WHAT?" GROWLS CEREBUS.

"YOUR HISTORY-- YOUR BOOK" HE EXPLAINS NASALLY.

"WHY DIDN'T YOU SAY 'BOOK' THE FIRST TIME," GRUMBLES THE AARDVARK

"I AM PLEASED TO INFORM YOU COMMA AS WELL COMMA THAT THE FORMER KITCHEN STAFF SUPERVISOR SLASH PRIME MINISTER WILL BE JOINING US PERIOD PLEASE CONTACT ME AT THE ADDRESS BELOW PERIOD YOURS TRULY ET CETERA," HE CONCLUDES.

"WELL, ENOUGH OF LETTER-WRITING," CRIES YOUNG SILVERSPOON CHEERFULLY, "NOW, YOU AND TRYSTRIM AND I MUST HAVE A GAME OF CARDS. GWANE DOESN'T PLAY." "DIAMONDBACK?" ASKS THE EARTH-PIG, MENTALLY LICKING HIS LIPS.

"HEAVENS NO--A GAME OF PRIESTESS! NO ONE PLAYS DIAMONDBACK ANYMORE," HE ADMONISHES DEPRECATINGLY.

"CEREBUS HAS NEVER HEARD OF IT" THE AARDVARK GRUMBLES. "IT'S EVER SO SIMPLE," ENTHUSES SILVERSPOON.

"EVEN YOU SHOULD BE ABLE TO UNDER-STAND IT" HE ADDS.

"WE EACH GET THREE CARDS. THE PRIESTESS IS WORTH FOUR, THE WHITE QUEEN IS WORTH PLUS TWO, THE BLACK QUEEN IS WORTH MINUS TWO. THE GOLD CARD DOUBLES THE VALUE OF THE PRIESTESS OR QUEEN CARDS OR, WITHOUT THEM, IS WORTH ONE POINT. THE SWORD CARD DOESN'T DO ANYTHING. THE SCEPTER CARD REDUCES THE PRIESTESS OR QUEEN CARDS TO HALF THEIR VALUE, OR, BY ITSELF, IS WORTH MINUS ONE. THE PRIEST CARD ADDS ONE TO THE FINAL TOTAL. WE EACH ANTE A CROWN, THEN THE DEALER MAKES AN INITIAL WAGER WHICH THE OTHER PLAYERS HAVE TO MATCH. THEN YOU DISCARD ONE AND TAKE ANOTHER FROM THE DECK, OR STAY WITH THE THREE YOU HAVE. THEN THE DEALER BETS AGAIN AND THE OTHER PLAYERS CAN MATCH THE BET OR RAISE IT AND WHEN THE BETTING IS OVER, WE DETERMINE WHO WON AND THE WINNER IS THE DEALER FOR THE NEXT HAND, UN-LESS THERE'S A TIE IN WHICH CASE THE TIED PLAYERS PLAY ANOTHER HAND TO DETERMINE WHO WINS THE POT AND THE DEALER

"CEREBUS DOESN'T HAVE ANY MONEY" MUTTERS CEREBUS EVASIVELY.

"DON'T BE SUCH A KILL-JOY" LECTURES THE YOUNG ARISTOCRAT. "I HAVE PLENTY TO GO AROUND."

"I'LL DEAL FIRST" HE OFFERS, RAPIDLY SHUFFLING THE CARDS.

"TWO CROWNS," WAGERS SILVERSPOON, IGNORING HIM.

"TWO CROWNS," CHIRPS TRYSTRIM, AGREEABLY.

"TWO CROWNS" ADDS CEREBUS, HAVING DECIDED THERE ARE WORSE THINGS IN LIFE THAN GAMBLING WITH SOMEONE ELSE'S MONEY.

"I'LL TAKE ONE" SAYS SILVERSPOON.

"ONE" SAYS TRYSTRIM.

"ONE" SAYS CEREBUS

"CEREBUS CAN'T STAND 'CUTE' CARD GAMES," SNARLS THE EARTH-PIG.

"THREE CROWNS" ASSERTS SILVERSPOON, HIS SCALP TINGLING WITH EXCITEMENT.

"THREE CROWNS" SNAPS TRYSTRIM, WITH GREAT GUSTO.

"THREE CROWNS" MUTTERS CEREBUS UNCERTAINLY...

"PRIESTESS, WHITE QUEEN, SWORD. THAT'S SIX," CHORTLES SILVERSPOON.

"SWORD, SWORD, PRIEST," SIGHS TRYSTRIM. "THAT'S ONE."

"BLACK QUEEN, GOLD, GOLD...MINUS...UH...EIGHT," MURMURS CEREBUS.

HIS COMPANIONS STIFLE IMPOLITE GIGGLES.

22

"TWO CROWNS," WAGERS SILVERSPOON, HOPING TO LIGHTEN THE MOOD. ②

"HA HA, TWO CROWNS," ANSWERS TRYSTRIM, FOLLOWING HIS LEAD. ③

"THIS DAMN GAME IS RIGGED" BELLOWS CEREBUS, HURLING TWO BLACK QUEENS AND A SWORD CARD INTO THE AIR.

"TWO DAMN CROWNS" GROWLS CEREBUS IN AN ATTEMPT TO RESTORE A FUNEREAL GRIMNESS.

"I THINK I SHALL STAY WITH THESE CARDS" WINKS SILVERSPOON PLAYFULLY.

"CEREBUS DOESN'T WANT TO PLAY ANYMORE," SULKS THE EARTH-PIG. "ONE MORE HAND," CAJOLES SILVERSPOON. "YOU'VE JUST HAD A BIT OF BAD LUCK." ④

"AND I, TOO" CHUCKLES TRYSTRIM, CARELESSLY SHAKING HIS CURLS. ⑤

"CEREBUS WILL TAKE ANOTHER DAMN CARD," HE SNAPS, THROUGH CLENCHED TEETH.

"WELL I NEVER" SNORTS SILVERSPOON. "OF ALL THE NERVE" CLUCKS TRYSTRIM. "AYE," AGREES GWANE AS THE TRIO LEAVE IN A HUFF (A FAVOURITE MEANS OF TRANSPORTATION).

⑥ ⑦

"FIVE CROWNS" WAGERS SILVERSPOON, HAPPILY.

"AND ANOTHER FIVE," RESPONDS TRYSTRIM WITH GLEE.

"ALE," SHOUTS THE EARTH-PIG, WAVING THE TWO CROWNS HE GOT FOR HIS PEN.

⑧ ⑨

THE NEXT DAY, HAVING BEEN PRESENTED WITH A BILL FOR FIVE DOZEN ALES (ONLY THREE DOZEN OF WHICH HE RECALLS), THE FORMER PRIME MINISTER ACCEPTS HIS FIRST JOB SINCE LEAVING THE EXECUTIVE MANSION; CLEANING OUT THE INN'S STABLES.

HE NOTES THAT THE TWO OCCUPATIONS ARE NOT, ESSENTIALLY, DISSIMILAR.

"AH, HERE YOU ARE," SMIRKS SILVERSPOON. "FINALLY FOUND A JOB YOU CAN HANDLE, HM?" THE EARTH-PIG MAKES NO REPLY.

"I REALLY SHOULDN'T FORGIVE YOU FOR YOUR RUDE BEHAVIOUR, BUT I AM POSSESSED OF A NEARLY SUPER-HUMAN NOBILITY OF SPIRIT," CONFIDES SILVERSPOON. "HOW WONDERFUL" SAYS CEREBUS, SNIDELY. "I'VE HAD WORD FROM THE COUNTESS. SHE ISN'T THRILLED ABOUT HAVING YOU, BUT I HAVE INSISTED BY RETURN POST THAT YOU BE PERMITTED TO JOIN US."

"NATURALLY, YOU WOULD HAVE TO PULL YOUR OWN WEIGHT," HE NOTES. "CARRY ALL THE LUGGAGE, RUN ERRANDS FOR FOR ME, DO LAUNDRY AND SUCH."

SUDDENLY, THE STABLE DOOR SWINGS INWARD.

"YOU'VE FOUND HIM! YOU'VE FOUND HIM!" SHRIEKS GWANE. "I WAS GETTING SO TERRIBLY WORRIED!" "GWANE." CAUTIONS SILVERSPOON.

"I MEAN, WHEN THE LETTER ARRIVED SAYING THE COUNTESS AGREED TO COVER OUR EXPENSES, BUT ONLY IF CEREBUS CAME WITH US," BURBLES GWANE.

"GWANE." SAYS SILVERSPOON, MENACINGLY.

"NOT TO MENTION THE FACT THAT SHE MADE THE BANK DRAUGHT PAYABLE TO CEREBUS..."

"OOWUMPH." HE ADDS AS SILVERSPOON'S ELBOW SINKS SHARPLY BENEATH HIS RIBS.

"HOW MUCH WAS THE BANK DRAUGHT FOR?" QUERIES THE EARTH-PIG. "FOUR HUNDRED CROWNS," ADMITS SILVERSPOON.

"MM. NOT ENOUGH." MUSES THE EARTH-PIG.

"NOT ENOUGH?" GASPS YOUNG SILVERSPOON.

"CEREBUS WOULD RATHER SHOVEL MANURE" REPLIES THE 'EARTH-PIG DIFFIDENTLY.

"BUT YOU CAN'T... YOU'LL RUIN... HOW CAN YOU POSSIBLY..." SPLUTTERS SILVERSPOON.

"CEREBUS LIKES SHOVELLING MANURE," HE ANSWERS CALMLY. "FOUR HUNDRED CROWNS JUST ISN'T ENOUGH MONEY."

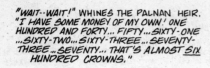

"WAIT—WAIT!" WHINES THE PALNAN HEIR. "I HAVE SOME MONEY OF MY OWN! ONE HUNDRED AND FORTY... FIFTY... SIXTY-ONE ...SIXTY-TWO...SIXTY-THREE...SEVENTY-THREE...SEVENTY... THAT'S ALMOST SIX HUNDRED CROWNS."

"WELL, I DON'T KNOW," CEREBUS PAUSES, "HMM."

"AND MY HAND-DRAWN DECK OF PRIESTESS CARDS," HE WHIMPERS. "YOU COULD SELL THEM FOR AT LEAST FIFTY-FIVE CROWNS."

"WELL, OKAY," ACQUIESCES THE EARTH-PIG, GRUDGINGLY. "WE'LL HAVE A WONDERFUL TIME," ENTHUSES YOUNG SILVERSPOON. "INDEED," AGREES GWANE. "SHE THROWS THE BEST PARTIES IN SEPRANIA PROVINCE."

"ACTUALLY, YOU'RE RIGHT," SAYS CEREBUS, BRIGHTLY. "SIX HUNDRED CROWNS IS A LOT OF MONEY. WE SHOULD BE ABLE TO HAVE A SPLENDID HOLIDAY." SILVERSPOON AND GWANE EAGERLY AGREE. "OH, YES," THEY CRY "A SPLENDID HOLIDAY."

AT THE DESK, CEREBUS (AFTER SETTLING HIS OWN ACCOUNT), ARRANGES PROVISIONS FOR A NOON DEPARTURE. "AN OPEN CARRIAGE, I SHOULD THINK, WITH A FOOTMAN AND DRIVER," ORDERS CEREBUS. "AND WHITE HORSES," SIMPERS SILVERSPOON. "WHITE HORSES, IT IS," AGREES THE EARTH-PIG. "VERY GOOD, SIR" GROVELS THE DESK CLERK.

"ASIDE FROM THAT, WE'LL NEED A BIG PICNIC BASKET FULL OF CUCUMBER SANDWICHES. NO CRUSTS," SPECIFIES CEREBUS. "AND WINE -- SOMETHING SORT OF STICKY AND SWEET." "STRAW-BERRY-FLAVOURED CHAMPAGNE, SIR?" "PERFECT," CONCLUDES CEREBUS.

"THIS IS GOING TO BE SUCH A FUN TRIP" THE YOUNG ARISTOCRATS EXCLAIM WITH DELIGHT. "I SHALL BE PLEASED TO MAKE ALL THE ARRANGEMENTS," SAYS THE DESK CLERK, HIS EYES LOCKED ON CEREBUS' WAD OF BANK NOTES.

"NOW YOU TWO SCOOT OFF TO BED," LECTURES CEREBUS "WE'RE LEAVING AT NOON TOMORROW." "WE'LL BE HERE," SHOUTS SILVERSPOON. "WITH BELLS ON," GIGGLES GWANE.

"MIGHT I RECOMMEND A CARRIAGE WITH RED VELVET UPHOLSTERY FOR M'LORD'S JOURNEY?" INQUIRES THE DESK CLERK.

"CANCEL ALL THAT JUNK AND GET CEREBUS A PLAIN BLACK CARRIAGE AND TEAM OF HORSES." BARKS THE EARTH-PIG. "HAVE THEM WAITING OUT FRONT IN TEN MINUTES."

"HERE'S A CROWN NOTE FOR YOUR TROUBLE."

"THANK YOU, SIR" SIGHS THE DESK CLERK.

NEXT: The Countess

28

CEREBUS in 'THE COUNTESS & THE AARDVARK'

30

31

ANY AMOUNT OF MONEY AT ALL...

HOW MUCH WOULD YOU WANT?

ALL OF IT.

NO--I MEAN WHAT AMOUNT?

OKAY, SAY IT WASN'T ME. SAY IT WAS LORD JULIUS... HOW MUCH WOULD YOU WANT THEN?

ALL OF IT.

MAYBE WE SHOULD TALK ABOUT SOMETHING ELSE...

WHAT DID YOU THINK OF CEREBUS' BOOK?

ALL OF IT-- WHATEVER YOU HAD.

IT'S OKAY...

I LIKED THE PART ABOUT THE BUTLER, HAVE YOU WRITTEN ANY MORE?

NO. CEREBUS JUST STARTED.

IS THAT WHAT YOU'RE HERE FOR?

HUH?

TO WRITE. IS THAT WHAT YOU'RE HERE FOR?

CEREBUS USUALLY WRITES IN BARS.

MONEY?

32

33

34

36

37

"On Governing"
by
Former Prime Minister
Cerebus of
Iest

PART the Third

1. Lord Julius

The first day that Cerebus was in Palnu, Lord Julius was meeting with the head of Palnu's taxation department. The guy wanted to know what rate of tax was going to be charged property-owners that year. Lord Julius asked Cerebus to pick a number between one and twenty. I said seventeen. So he turns and tells the guy that it will be seventeen per cent. That pretty well sums up the kind of leader that Lord Julius is. Another time someone came and told him that the clean-up crews in the Trade Building were over-staffed and half of them were lying around with nothing to do. So, Lord Julius orders twenty gallons of paint from the supply room and has it sent to the lobby. If you have ever seen the lobby of the trade building, it is HUGE!! He calls in the Trade Building guards and tells them to cover the lobby with this paint, see? (Which is a sort of greenish-yellow colour). Here are these Trade Building guards spraying paint all over the marble columns and the inlaid floor. They must have thrown paint around for an hour and a half -- no kidding. Finally Lord Julius tells them to stop and leaves instructions that the paint is to be allowed to dry overnight and then the clean-up crew is to be given one day to clean it up or half of them would be fired. When they got it all done in time, he decided that they were over-staffed and fired half of them anyway. When people ask Cerebus what Lord Julius is like, this is what Cerebus thinks of. He's not very tall, but everyone does whatever he says right away. Except Cerebus. Cerebus used to ask "why" all the time, until Lord Julius would get tired of explaining and then he would go and ask someone else to do it.

Cerebus helped to stop a revolution by the "Eye in the Pyramid," but the more Cerebus thinks about it, the more it seems that Lord Julius probably planned the whole revolution himself.

He also has a painted-on mustache instead of a real one.

LOOKS LIKE THE RAIN'S LETTING UP...

DO YOU REALLY THINK *LORD JULIUS'* SON CAN GET ME A *DEFERRAL* ON MY TAXES?...

NO -- BUT CEREBUS *CAN*...

REALLY? HOW...?

CEREBUS STILL HAS FRIENDS IN *PANU.* IT'LL TAKE SOME GREASING OF THE WHEELS... BUT CEREBUS *CAN* GET IT *DONE*...

HOW MUCH "GREASE" ARE WE TALKING ABOUT?

A FEW HUNDRED...

MAYBE A THOUSAND AT THE MOST...

THAT'S PRETTY *GOOD*...

THAT'S NOT *BAD* AT ALL...

I'VE ALREADY SENT FIVE HUNDRED TO THE TRADE BUILDING FOR A *DIRECTORY* OF TAX OFFICIALS...

AND I *STILL* HAVEN'T *SEEN* IT...

WHY WON'T YOU TELL CEREBUS WHETHER YOU'RE A *CIRINIST* OR A *KEVILLIST?*

41

43

44

46

48

THE ORIGIN OF THE WOLVEROACH

50

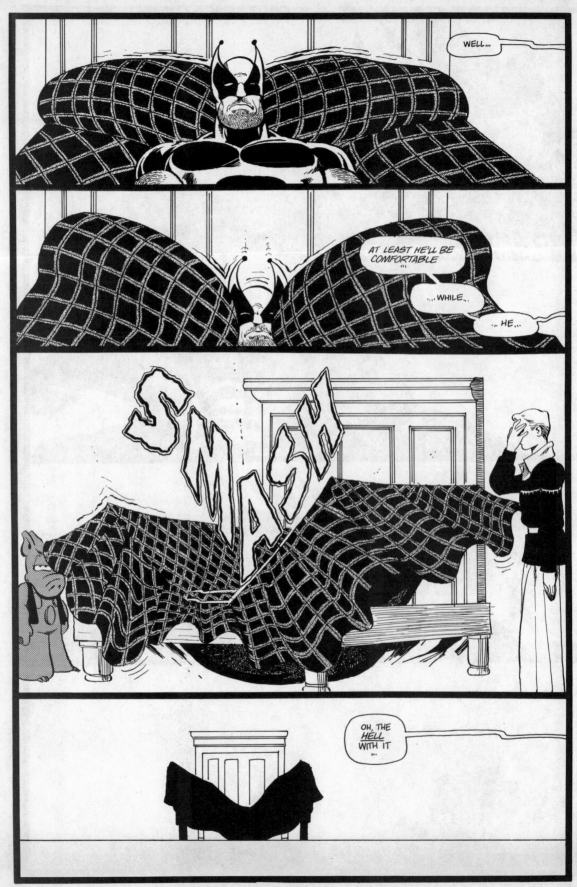

YOU'RE SURE YOU DON'T WANT TO JUST DRINK IT STRAIGHT OUT OF THE *BOTTLE?*

THAT WOULDN'T BE *POLITE* ...

YOU'VE GOT *MORE* OF IT, I HOPE ...

I'VE GOT ANOTHER *CASE* IN THE BASEMENT ...

GETTING BACK TO YOUR *QUESTION,* THE FIRST TIME I SAW *ARTEMIS,* WEISSHAUPT BROUGHT HIM TO MY *WINTER HOME* IN BEDUIN ...

HE ASKED ME IF I'D MIND *HARBOURING* THE NOTORIOUS *"COCKROACH"* -- BEDUIN'S MOST DESPERATE CRIMINAL ...

HE LOOKED *MORE* LIKE AN OLD *CIRCUS ACROBAT* WHO HADN'T SLEPT IN A FEW WEEKS

BUT I'M A SUCKER FOR CONTROVERSY, SO I SAID *"SURE"* ...

"FOR THE FIRST FEW DAYS, IT WAS GREAT... ANYTIME I NEEDED A JAR OPENED, HE WAS RIGHT THERE, GRABBING THE TOP WITH HIS FINGERS AND SNAPPING IT OFF. MIND YOU, HE DID THE SAME THING WITH THE SCREW-ON LIDS, BUT IT WAS THE THOUGHT THAT COUNTED. HE USED TO TELL ME ABOUT HIMSELF -- OR HE WOULD TRY TO ANYWAY. SOMETIMES IT WOULDN'T MAKE MUCH SENSE..."

"THE PEOPLE WHO KILLED HIS PARENTS SAWED THROUGH THE ORPHANAGE HE WAS SENT TO, KILLING ALL OF HIS LITTLE FRIENDS, BUT WEISSHAUPT HAD A SECRET FORMULA THAT WOULD MAKE THEM PAY..."

"WEISSHAUPT CAME AND GOT HIM LATER THAT WEEK AND I DIDN'T SEE ARTEMIS AGAIN UNTIL THE FOLLOWING WINTER--1412"

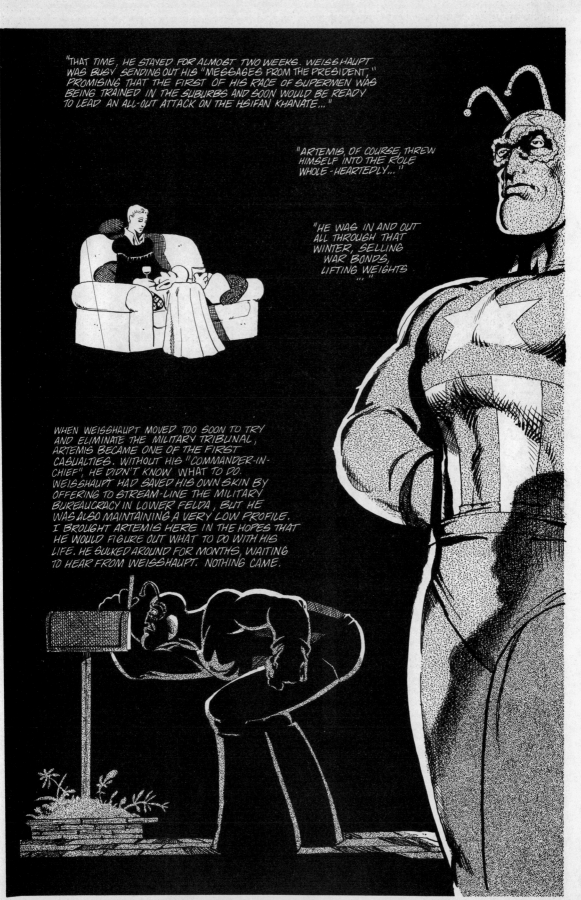

"THAT TIME, HE STAYED FOR ALMOST TWO WEEKS. WEISSHAUPT WAS BUSY SENDING OUT HIS "MESSAGES FROM THE PRESIDENT," PROMISING THAT THE FIRST OF HIS RACE OF SUPERMEN WAS BEING TRAINED IN THE SUBURBS AND SOON WOULD BE READY TO LEAD AN ALL-OUT ATTACK ON THE HSIFAN KHANATE..."

"ARTEMIS, OF COURSE, THREW HIMSELF INTO THE ROLE WHOLE-HEARTEDLY..."

"HE WAS IN AND OUT ALL THROUGH THAT WINTER, SELLING WAR BONDS, LIFTING WEIGHTS ..."

WHEN WEISSHAUPT MOVED TOO SOON TO TRY AND ELIMINATE THE MILITARY TRIBUNAL, ARTEMIS BECAME ONE OF THE FIRST CASUALTIES. WITHOUT HIS "COMMANDER-IN-CHIEF", HE DIDN'T KNOW WHAT TO DO. WEISSHAUPT HAD SAVED HIS OWN SKIN BY OFFERING TO STREAM-LINE THE MILITARY BUREAUCRACY IN LOWER FELDA, BUT HE WAS ALSO MAINTAINING A VERY LOW PROFILE. I BROUGHT ARTEMIS HERE IN THE HOPES THAT HE WOULD FIGURE OUT WHAT TO DO WITH HIS LIFE. HE SULKED AROUND FOR MONTHS, WAITING TO HEAR FROM WEISSHAUPT. NOTHING CAME.

"THEN, ONE DAY, ASTORIA SHOWED UP AT THE DOOR. SHE SAID SHE NEEDED A PLACE TO STAY, AND COULD I PUT HER UP FOR A FEW DAYS? I HADN'T SEEN HER SINCE SHE AND LORD JULIUS STAYED HERE WITH THE COUNT AND I JUST BEFORE THEY GOT DIVORCED. I THOUGHT SHE AND UNCLE ARTEMIS WOULDN'T GET ALONG, BUT THEY DID. THEY'D SIT OUT IN THE GARDEN BY THE HOUR, JUST TALKING AWAY..."

"SOON, ARTEMIS STOPPED RANTING ABOUT THE RED CLAW CULTISTS AND THE UNITED FELDWAR STATES. HE BEGAN TALKING ABOUT BANKING AND ECONOMICS. HE SAID HE WANTED TO HELP ALL THE PEOPLE WHO HAD BEEN HURT BY LORD JULIUS' HIGH INTEREST RATES. HE SAID THAT ASTORIA HAD SOME FRIENDS BACK EAST WHO WERE TRYING TO CHANGE THINGS... TRYING TO MAKE THE RULES FAIRER. IT SEEMED TO ME THAT HE HAD FINALLY FOUND SOMETHING IN THE REAL WORLD TO GET INTERESTED IN."

"UNTIL I READ HIS FAREWELL NOTE THE NEXT MORNING"

"HE WAS GOING TO IEST TO STAMP OUT ECONOMIC INJUSTICE... HE DIDN'T KNOW WHEN HE WOULD BE BACK. HE DID SAY HE WOULD CONTACT ME WHEN ASTORIA GAVE HIM A NEW ORIGIN. I KNEW, THEN, HE WAS JUST BEING USED AGAIN..."

DEAR COWNTESS
I AM GOING TO IEST TO HELP STAMP OUT ECONOMIC INJUSTICE. THANK YOU FOR LETING ME STAY AT YOUR HOUSE

"OVER THE COURSE OF THE NEXT FEW MONTHS, HE WOULD APPEAR IN ONE OF THE WINDOWS FROM TIME TO TIME -- USUALLY ON THE SECOND FLOOR -- I GUESS HE THOUGHT IT WAS MORE IMPRESSIVE THAT WAY OR SOMETHING. HE'D STARTED CHANGING HIS PERSONALITIES FASTER AND FASTER..."

"READING BETWEEN THE LINES, I COULD SEE THAT ASTORIA HAD DROPPED HIM WHEN YOU CAME ALONG. HE WAS CRUSHED, BUT COULDN'T SHOW IT --. HE TOLD ME HOW HE PLOTTED AGAINST THE TWO OF YOU. BUT, WHEN ASTORIA MADE HIM YOUR BODYGUARD, HE ACCEPTED IT HAPPILY, THINKING SHE WANTED HIM BACK."

"WHEN YOUR GOVERNMENT FELL, ALL I COULD THINK WAS 'POOR ARTEMIS'. I KNEW THAT ASTORIA WOULDN'T LIFT A FINGER TO SAVE HIM. A FEW DAYS LATER, I GOT A LETTER FROM THE ASSISTANT TO THE ARCHBISHOP, A FATHER ARTEMIS ROACH, ADVISING ME TO FORSAKE MY SORDID LIFESTYLE AND GIVE ALL MY HICKIES TO THE LIVING TARIM."

"THE LETTER REASSURED ME THAT HE WAS -- I WOULDN'T SAY 'OKAY' -- BUT AT LEAST 'NOT IN ANY PHYSICAL DANGER'"

A VERY PRETTY LITTLE STORY, MY DEAR...

59

60

I SAVED THAT LITTLE SURPRISE JUST FOR YOU, MY DEAR... I WANTED YOU TO BE THE FIRST TO KNOW...

YOU ARE TOO KIND...

ESPECIALLY YOURS.

THEY ALWAYS HAVE THE AMBIENCE OF CHEAP MELODRAMA ABOUT THEM...

THE COUNTESS SIMPLY ADORES HEARING ABOUT ALL OF THE LATEST INTRIGUES...

YOU'LL FIND, MY DEAR -- AS YOU GROW OLDER -- THAT TRUE MELODRAMA NEVER COMES CHEAP...

...ASSUMING THAT I EVER GIVE IT A SECOND THOUGHT...

SO YOU FIGURE LORD JULIUS WILL MAKE THE DIFFERENCE?...

THE ENTIRE COALITION IS WHAT WILL MAKE THE DIFFERENCE... LORD JULIUS, THE EASTERN CHURCH, THE MERCHANT CLASS, LAND-OWNERS...

MOST COUNTRIES EXIST BECAUSE OF ETHNIC DIFFERENCES OR GEOGRAPHY. OURS WILL BE DEDICATED TO MAKING US ALL WEALTHY BEYOND OUR WILDEST DREAMS...

THAT'S WHY YOU ASKED CEREBUS IF HE BELIEVED IN *REPUBLICANISM* ...

EXACTLY. YOU START GIVING THE VOTE TO *PEASANTS* AND *LIVESTOCK* AND BEFORE YOU KNOW IT, THE WHOLE SCHEME GOES UP THE CHIMNEY...

SO WHERE DOES THE *BUG* FIT INTO ALL THIS?

THE ...?

OH. HIM.

THE OBJECTIVE WAS TO CREATE A *POPULAR HERO* FOR THE *PEASANTS* AND *LIVESTOCK.* IF YOU DON'T WANT TO SHARE YOUR POWER WITH THEM, YOU BETTER HAVE SOMETHING HANDY TO *DISTRACT* THEM ...

THE MISTAKE I MADE WITH *CAPTAIN COCKROACH* WAS TO MAKE HIM A *GOVERNMENT MASCOT* AND A *MILITARY* FIGURE. NO ONE TRUSTS THE GOVERNMENT AND NO ONE TRUSTS THE *MILITARY*...

THE MISTAKE *ASTORIA* MADE WITH THE *MOON ROACH* WAS TO MAKE HIM AN ORDINARY KILLER... SHE ONLY MANAGED TO INCREASE THE *NERVOUSNESS* IN HIGH PLACES...

WHEN THAT *NERVOUS-NESS* REACHED A *CRESCENDO,* SHE WAS FORCED TO ELIMINATE THE *GRAND INQUISITOR* SINCE HE WAS ABOUT TO TAKE *ACTION*...

SO, WHEN THAT *RIDICULOUS* ELECTION WAS CALLED AND YOU WON, SHE WAS STUCK WITH A CHAP WHOSE ONLY FUNCTION WAS TO *UPSET* THE *NATURAL ORDER* WHICH SHE NOW *CONTROLLED*...

WITH NOTHING TO DO, HE QUICKLY GREW FLACCID, *PAUNCHY*...

64

"LIKE CAPTAIN COCKROACH, HE'S A PRODUCT OF A SCIENTIFIC BREAKTHROUGH. POSSESSING ENORMOUS STRENGTH, HE WAS KIDNAPPED BY THE FOUNDING FATHERS OF THE UNITED FELDWAR STATES WHO REPLACED HIS SKELETON WITH ONE MADE OF LEAD FOR EVEN GREATER STRENGTH..."

"OH, COME ON! A METAL SKELETON? NO ONE WOULD BELIEVE THAT..."

THE SCENARIO OF THE WOLVEROACH COMBINES THE BEST ELEMENTS OF THE THREE PREVIOUS INCARNATIONS. LIKE THE COCKROACH, HE'S A CRAZED LONE WOLF; EVERYONE ADMIRES THE ONE WHO MAKES HIS OWN RULES, NO MATTER HOW STUPID THE RULES MAY BE...ACTUALLY, THE 'STUPIDER' THEY ARE, THE GREATER THE ADMIRATION...

" OH, QUITE THE CONTRARY. A FRIEND ONCE ASKED IF IT WAS TRUE THAT NO POLITICIAN EVER FAILED BY UNDERESTIMATING THE INTELLIGENCE OF THE PEASANTS AND LIVESTOCK. I TOLD HIM WE WOULD NEVER KNOW, BECAUSE THEIR INTELLIGENCE WAS SOMETHING THAT WAS IMPOSSIBLE TO UNDERESTIMATE..."

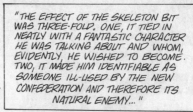

"THE EFFECT OF THE SKELETON BIT WAS THREE-FOLD. ONE, IT TIED IN NEATLY WITH A FANTASTIC CHARACTER HE WAS TALKING ABOUT AND WHOM, EVIDENTLY, HE WISHED TO BECOME. TWO, IT MADE HIM IDENTIFIABLE AS SOMEONE ILL-USED BY THE NEW CONFEDERATION AND THEREFORE ITS NATURAL ENEMY..."

"AND, THREE, IT GAVE ME THE EXCUSE I NEED TO HAVE TWO HUNDRED POUNDS OF MOLDED LEAD STITCHED INTO HIS COSTUME TO HELP TURN HIS FLAB BACK INTO MUSCLE..."

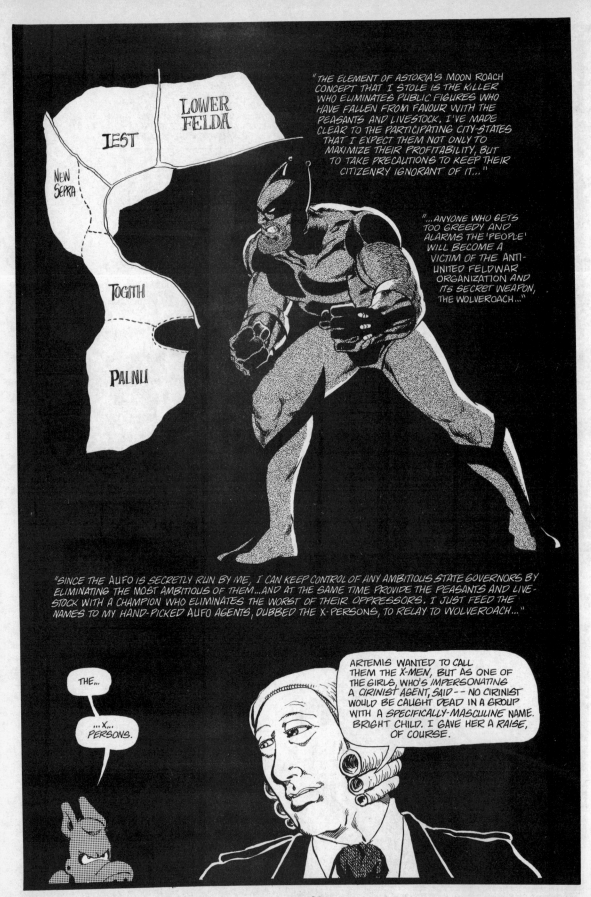

CLICK

"DEFINITE MAYBE"?

I SWEAR THAT MAN WENT TO SCHOOL TO LEARN HOW TO EXIT ...

-- THE ROOM!

HUH?

I PUT THEM BOTH IN THE SAME ROOM!

WHO?

WHUT HAVE YUH DONE TUH MUH BEDDY-ROOM Y'LONG EAR'D JOCK-STRAP?!

SNIKT

OH.

SNIKT!

OUCHY! AH THINK Y'BUSTED MUH LAIG Y'LEOTARD W'ARIN' BIMBO!

SNIKT SNIKT

WUMP!

DOUBLE OUCHY --NOW YUH BUSTED MUH OTHER LAIG

SNIKT SNIKT SNIKT

STAND STILL, VARMINT-- AHM FIXIN' TUH GNAW ON YER INSTEP...

ORIGIN OF THE WOLVEROACH

PART 2

THE WHY & THE ARE

76

"On Governing" PART the FOURTH
by Cerebus, former Prime
Minister of Iest

Power

Power is a very strange thing. When you
are Prime Minister, no one can say "no" to
you or you have them executed. But there
are different ways of saying "no". You can
tell Cerebus you are "studying the matter"
or that you are "encountering problems."
If you are told to do it Cerebus' way,
you'll go away grumbling and you
won't do a good job because you want
to prove Cerebus was wrong to tell you
to do it that way. So Cerebus has the
choice of getting a job done right
your way, or done wrong Cerebus'
way. The longer Cerebus went through
this crap, the more he realized why Lord
Julius runs Palnu the way he does.
No one listens anyway, so why try
to make sense? An aide came in and
said "The Abbess is revolting." Cerebus
waggled his eyebrows and said "I'll
say she is," and he went away.
    That was when Cerebus realized
that he was not going to last very
long as Prime Minister if he didn't
start drinking more...

slam

If no one is screaming at you, you are making good decisions. If you start making bad decisions, the only thing you can do is drink. You just keep making decisions and drinking, making decisions and drinking. Finally someone else takes care of it. But be sure to have some hot towels, raw eggs and a Blacksmith's vice handy for the next morning. If you are going to yell at people yourself, save it for when you have a hangover. You just keep yelling louder and louder and your head hurts more and more and finally you can't take it anymore, so you hurl yourself across your desk and land on the wimp's chest and pound him in the head until he dies. This is always a great tension reducer. It was Cerebus' cleaning lady who pointed out that you should always do this on tile, as the stains on the carpet are very hard to remove.

CLIK CLAK

clik
clak

ALL RIGHT -- WHAT DID YOU DO WITH ARTEMIS?

CEREBUS DIDN'T DO ANYTHING WITH ARTEMIS ...

WELL -- I HOPE YOU'RE SATISFIED..!

HE'S GONE..!

80

82

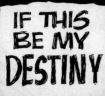

ORIGIN OF THE WOLVEROACH

PART 3

THE MYSTIC WE

SNIKT

TERROR IN A TINY DRIVEWAY!

SNIKT SNIKT

THE WOLVEROACH STRIKES BACK!

D'CROSSABOWS-A BOLTS -- DEY JUST-A-BOUNCING OFF...

HE'S-A NOT-A HUMAN!

SPWANG!

TUNG

TWANG

90

CHARLES X. CLAREMONT?

BUT YOU'RE DEAD!

DEAD!? NONSENSE, CHILD; BEING CRUSHED BETWEEN MY APOCALYPSE BEASTS* MERELY TRANSFORMED ME INTO A NEAR-*DEITY*...

HOWEVER...

MY PHYSICAL FORM, AFTER UNDERGOING THE *ORDEAL*, WAS IN NO CONDITION TO HOUSE MY *OMNIPOTENCE*!...

...SO I'VE BORROWED BOZO HERE FOR A WHILE...

* YES, THAT ISSUE --dave

LOOK-- NOT TO PUT TOO FINE A POINT ON IT, BUT I HAVE THESE *PLANS*

SO! I'M GOING TO HAVE TO ASK YOU TO TAKE YOUR LEAVE OF THE COUNTESS...

MIND!?

OF COURSE CEREBUS MINDS

WHO DO YOU THINK YOU...

SHE DOESN'T *LOVE* YOU, YOU KNOW.

I'M SURE YOU UNDERSTAND...

I HOPE YOU DON'T *MIND*...

95

96

GULP
GULP
GULP

GULP
GULP
GULP

OH. THAT IDEA.

ACTUALLY, THAT'S NOT A BAD IDEA YOU JUST HAD.

TELL HER THINGS HAVE TO GO *YOUR* *WAY* OR YOU'RE LEAVING...

I NEVER THOUGHT OF IT...

REMEMBER WHAT HAPPENED IN *IEST*...YOU LET EVERYONE ELSE RUN THE SHOW... IF YOU DON'T *TAKE* CONTROL YOU *RELINQUISH* IT...

CONTROL!

AYE! THAT'S IT...

IDEA?

WHAT IDEA?

BUT...

HAVE ANOTHER *DRINK*...

GULP! GULP!

AN ULTIMATUM.

AYE... AYE...

CONTROL!

LAY IT ON THE LINE FOR HER--TELL HER SHE CAN'T PRETEND THERE'S NOTHING GOING ON...

GOOD... GOOOD...

TAP TAP TAP

FIRST, CEREBUS WILL MOVE INTO THE *MASTER* BEDROOM WITH YOU...

CRACK CRACKLE CRACK

GOOD START

plop

THAT WILL LET EVERYONE KNOW THAT IT'S CEREBUS WHO'S PROTECTING YOU...

TAP TAP TAP

DON'T LET UP; SHE'S *REALLY* AFRAID OF LOSING YOU, NOW!

CRACK CRACKLE CRACK

IT WOULD BE BETTER IF YOU DIDN'T HAVE SO MANY VISITORS, TOO

IT LOOKS BAD ...

plop

DON'T FORGET THE BANK ACCOUNT ...

TAP TAP TAP

OH, RIGHT. CEREBUS WANTS ACCESS TO YOUR BANK ACCOUNT, TOO...

CRACK CRACKLE CRACK

COMPROMISE, NOW-- THE KITCHEN!

TAP
TAP
TAP

CRACK
CRACKLE
CRACK

EGG SALAD. WOULD YOU LIKE SOME?

THE KITCHEN WILL BE YOUR TERRITORY... CEREBUS CAN'T TELL YOU WHAT TO DO IN THE KITCHEN. _EVER._

ASK HER WHAT SHE'S MAKING.

WHAT ARE YOU MAKING?

MASH
MASH

MASH
MASH

SURE.

SURE.

IT DIDN'T WORK.
THE GULLIBILITY OF MERE MORTALS NEVER CEASES TO ASTOUND.
YOU'VE BEEN TRICKED, MY DIM-WITTED YOUNG FRIEND -- HORN-SWOGGLED, BAMBOOZLED, FLIM-FLAMMED...
HUH?
I LIED.
SHE WASN'T AFRAID OF LOSING CEREBUS?
YOU'RE JUST LUCKY SHE WASN'T STILL SLICING BREAD, WHEN YOU TOLD HER SHE COULD RUN THE KITCHEN.
YOU KNOW, FOR SOMEONE SO UTTERLY UNIQUE, YOU DISPLAY A SIMPLY APPALLING PENCHANT FOR MISPLACING YOUR LOYALTIES...
AND NOW YOU'RE DONE, AS THEY SAY, LIKE DINNER ...
YOU'VE LOST HER...
ACCEPT THAT.
GO BACK TO YOUR ORIGINAL IDEA ...
WHAT ORIGINAL IDEA?

113

116

117

123

125

126

BOOK TWO
Back to Iest

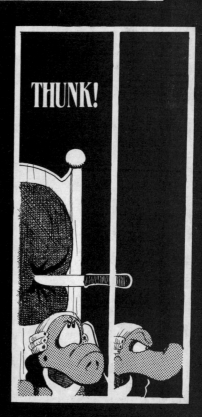

CEREBUS DARLING...?
ARE YOU AWAKE? ...
I HAVE TO TALK ...
DO IT IN THE LIVING ROOM-- CEREBUS IS TRYING TO SLEEP.
NONO!
I MEAN I HAVE TO TALK TO YOU...
CEREBUS WAS AFRAID OF THAT ...

SNFX
HUH?
WHA'
BURROW
BURROW
MMM.. HOW COME YOU'RE ALWAYS SO WARMMM? ...
IT'S CEREBUS' ONLY DEFENCE AGAINST YOUR HANDS GIVING HIM FROSTBITE ...
TELL ME HONESTLY.. DO YOU THINK MR. BLAKELY WANTS TO MARRY MY MOTHER...?
YOU'RE KIDDING.
SHE'S AFRAID OF GROWING OLD ALONE -- I CAN TELL...
YOUR MOTHER IS A VICIOUS FAT OLD UGLY WOMAN. NO ONE WANTS TO MARRY A VICIOUS OLD FAT UGLY WOMAN...

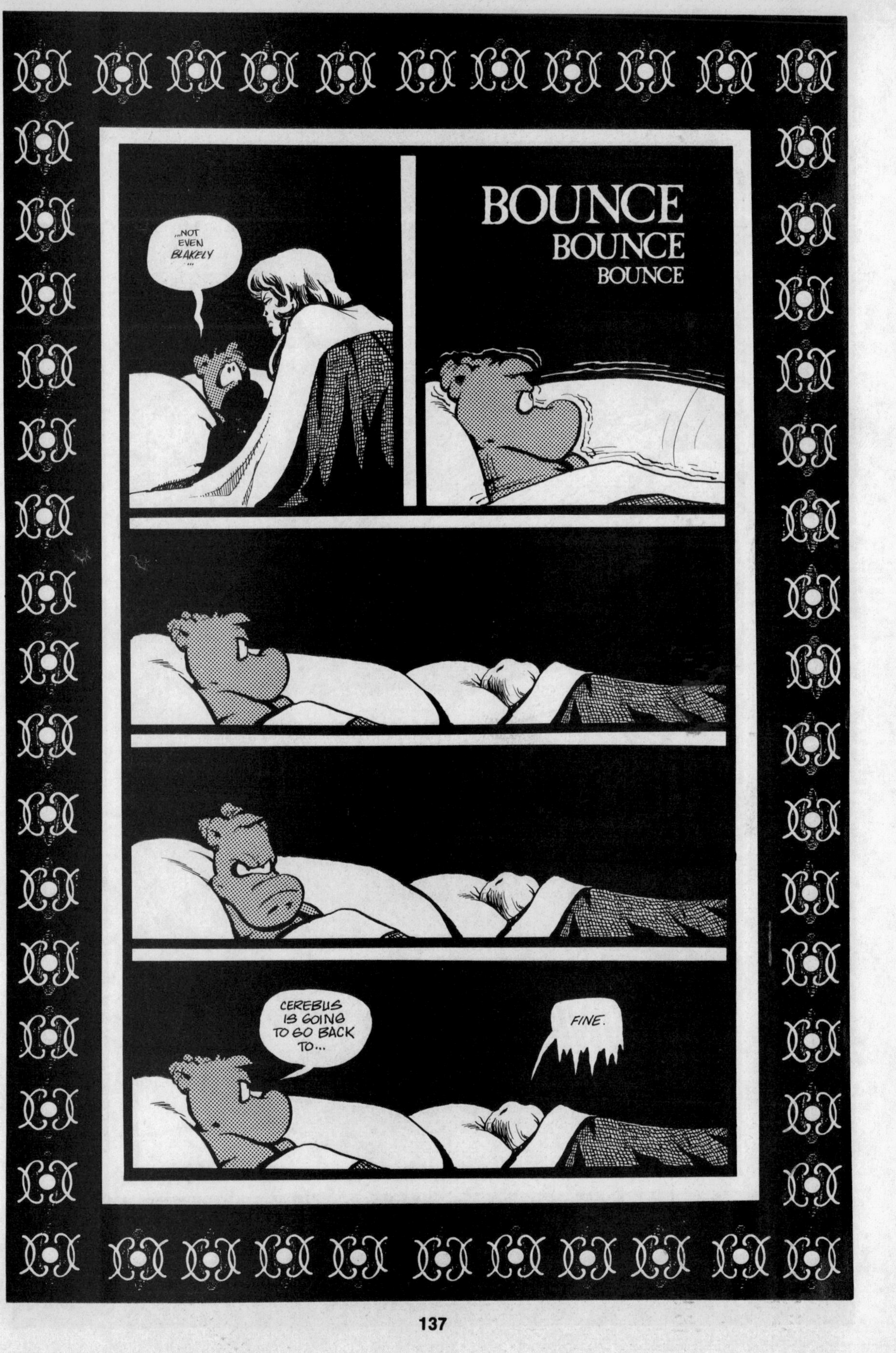

...NOT EVEN BLAKELY ...
BOUNCE
BOUNCE
BOUNCE
CEREBUS IS GOING TO GO BACK TO...
FINE.

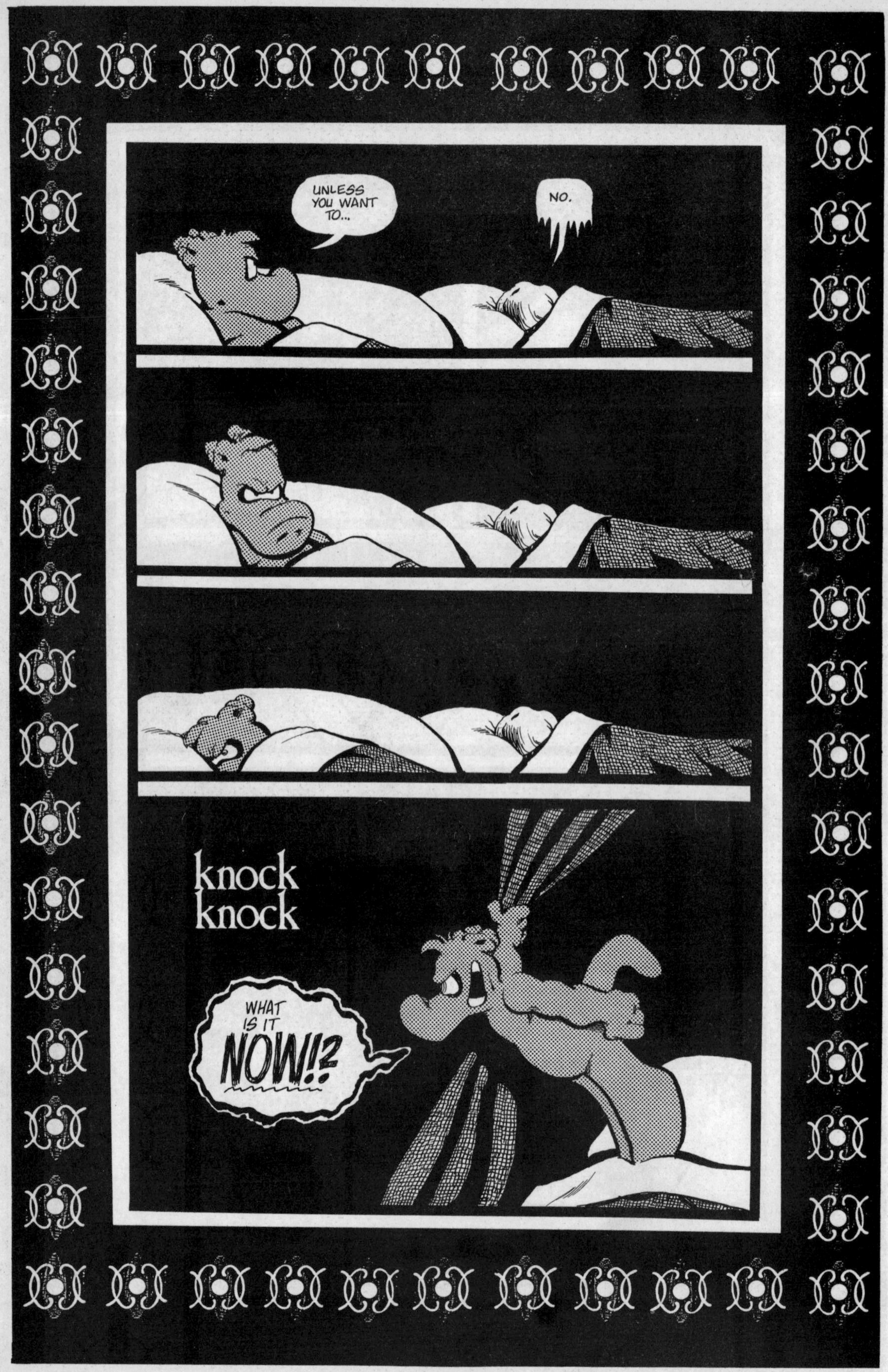
UNLESS YOU WANT TO...
NO.
knock knock
WHAT IS IT NOW!?

A-- REQUEST FOR A BRIEF MEETING ...
FROM HIS HOLINESS POPE HARMONY IV
HARMONY IV?
YOU MEAN HARMONY II.
POPE HARMONY II WAS EXECUTED A WEEK AFTER YOU RESIGNED, MR. PRIME MINISTER ...
THEN THE NEW ONE SHOULD BE HARMONY III...
NO, MR. PRIME MINISTER -- HARMONY III WAS EXECUTED BY "THE NEW ONE."
A MONTH OR SO AGO...
OH.
HE'D LIKE TO SPEAK TO YOU, PRIVATELY, IN THE CENTRAL TOWER...
WITH A REPRESENTATIVE OF "THE LION OF SERREA" IN ATTENDANCE, OF COURSE...

of course.
CEREBUS WILL BE READY IN A FEW MINUTES ...
CEREBUS IS GOING TO MEET THE ...
I HEARD.
WHEN CEREBUS GETS BACK, DO YOU WANT TO...
NO.

141

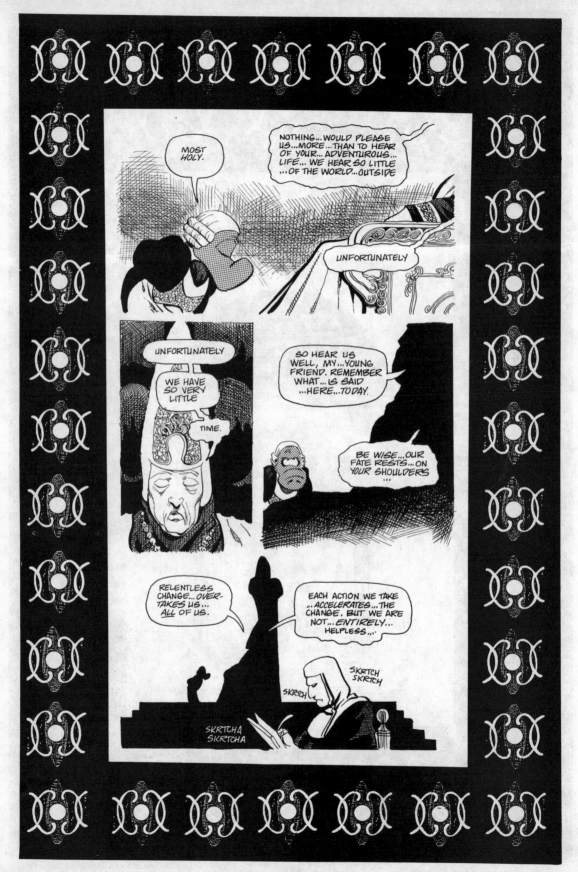

142

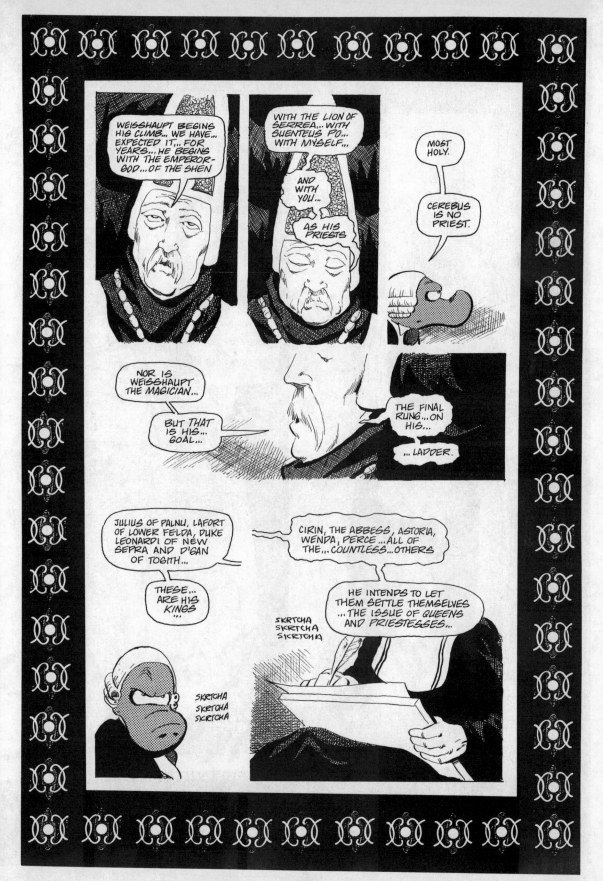

143

A LIVE BIRTH IS THE ONLY SUITABLE MEASURE OF A CITIZEN'S WORTH

ONE LIVE BIRTH...

ONE VOTE...

THE RIGHT TO OWN LAND...

THE RIGHT TO HANDLE CURRENCY ...

TO OWN MEN.

SKETCHA SKETCHA SKETCHA STEE...

ESTARCION HAS BEEN, FOR GENERATIONS, IN THE HANDS OF KINGS AND PRIESTS ...

COURTING PRIESTESSES AND OWNING QUEENS ...

THE PRIESTESSES HAVE GROWN COMPLACENT

BUT THE VOICE OF THE QUEENS GROWS STRONGER ...

WEISSHAUPT... UNDERESTIMATES THAT VOICE.... HE WATCHES THE VALUE OF UPPER FELDA'S CURRENCY.... STUDIES REPORTS OF HER MILITARY STRENGTH...

BUT HE DOES NOT HEAR THE VOICE...

HE THINKS HIS ...NEW TOY... WILL STILL THE VOICE ...

WHEN ALL IT WILL DO IS...

INCREASE THE CASUALTIES ...

BECAUSE IT IS CIRIN-- NOT WEISSHAUPT WHO WILL PREVAIL ...

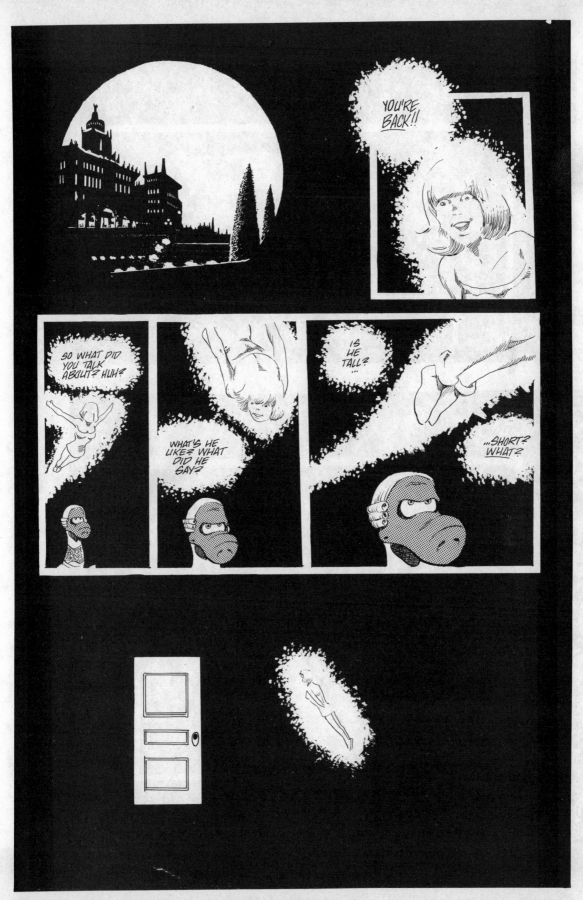

CARROLL E. KING READS

152

ONE AFTERNOON

MEMOIRS

"On Governing" PART the FIFTH
by Cerebus, Permanent Prime Minister of
Iest

Responsibility

    Everyone says that having power is a great responsibility. This is a lot of bunk. Responsibility is when someone can blame you if something goes wrong. When you have power you are surrounded by people whose job it is to take the blame for your mistakes. If they're smart, that is. Some of Cerebus' staff used to insist on only taking the blame for their _own_ mistakes. Cerebus had a bunch of them charged with treason and executed. At the very next meeting, one of Cerebus' mistakes was mentioned and Cerebus asked whose fault is this? Every hand in the room went up, Cerebus told them all not to let it happen again and we moved on to other mistakes.

    Teamwork and loyalty are the cornerstones of good government.

Like, for instance, there was nothing Cerebus could do about the economy. Lord Julius set the interest rates and decided how much Iest's crown was worth. As soon as the staff and Cerebus' cabinet realized that everything wrong with the economy was Lord Julius' fault, we started having more meetings about it. Cerebus would say "What are we going to do about high interest rates?" Everyone would shrug and say "What can we do? Lord Julius is the one who sets the rate." Cerebus would look thoughtful and say "That's true. Our hands are tied." Then everyone would nod and shrug their shoulders at once.

Unity is another cornerstone of good government

Once some new guy said "Why don't we try to beat Lord Julius at his own game?" Cerebus threw a paperweight at him and knocked him cold. The next meeting we had on the economy, he shrugged and nodded in all the right places so Cerebus had his wife and children released and dropped the treason charge against him.

WHAT DO YOU THINK?

I LIKED THE PART ABOUT THE *BUTLER*...

HAVE YOU WRITTEN ANY *MORE*?

note

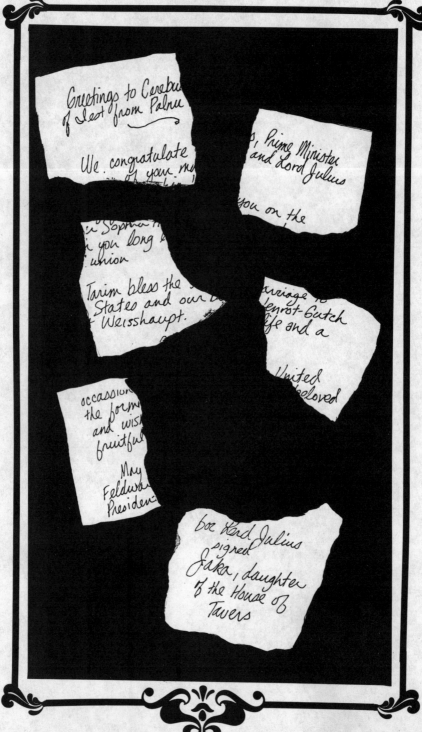

FIRST IMPRESSION

160

TREE PLANTING

162

165

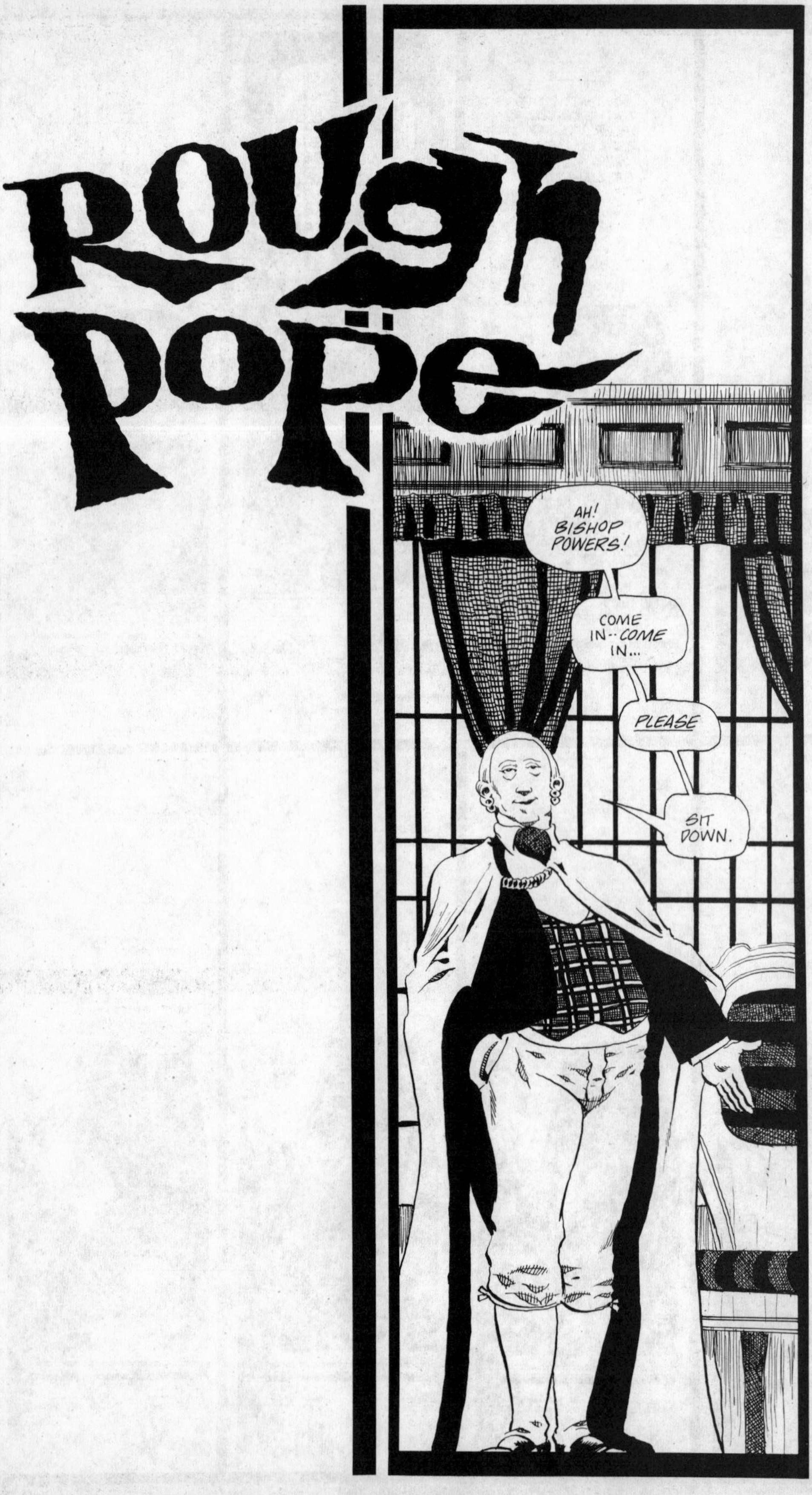
ROUGH POPE
AH! BISHOP POWERS!
COME IN--COME IN...
PLEASE
SIT DOWN.

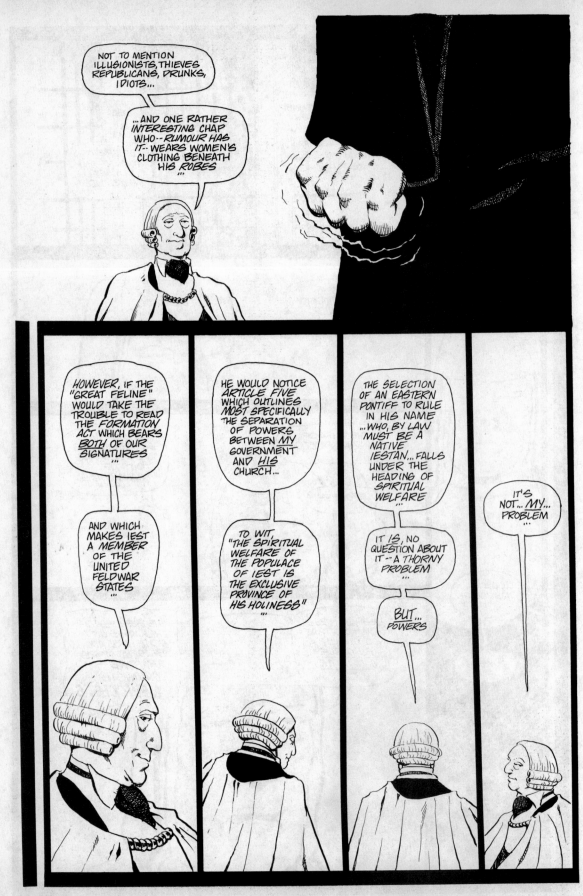

168

SOPHIA

SURE ENOUGH, FIFTEEN MINUTES LATER, YOU'RE TIRED OF BEING LEFT ALONE AND YOU COME BACK IN THE BEDROOM LOOKING LIKE SOMEONE JUST SHOT YOUR BEST FRIEND AND YOU SAY SOMETHING LIKE, "YOU DON'T _WANT_ TO STAY WITH CEREBUS, _DO YOU?_"

WHICH IS REALLY _WEIRD_, SINCE THE REASON THAT YOU BECAME THE PRIME MINISTER IS THAT YOU _SUPPOSEDLY_ WANT A _DIVORCE_...

SO _I_ SAY, "I'LL STAY HERE UNTIL SOMETHING BETTER COMES ALONG, SAME AS _YOU_."

AND THEN _YOU_ SAY "YOU'RE ONLY STAYING HERE BECAUSE OF ALL OF THE _FREE_ MONEY AND _SERVANTS_ AND CHOCOLATE AND _SPICES_."

AND THEN _I_ SAY "SURE I AM. SAME AS YOU."

THAT'S _USUALLY_ WHEN YOU BREAK SOMETHING BIG AND FRAGILE THAT MAKES AN AWFUL MESS. AND THEN I START TO CLEAN IT UP AND YOU SAY "WE HAVE SERVANTS FOR THAT."

SO I SIGNAL ONE OF THE SERVANTS TO COME IN AND THEY START CLEANING UP THE MESS AND I SAY TO YOU "DON'T THINK ABOUT *ME* -- DO *YOU* WANT TO LEAVE OR NOT?" AND THEN *YOU* SAY "CEREBUS DOESN'T WANT TO DISCUSS THIS IN FRONT OF THE SERVANTS"

SO, THEN I ASK YOU *AGAIN*, THIS TIME IN *BOREALAN*, "LOOK, DO YOU WANT TO LEAVE, YES OR NO?" AND THAT'S WHEN YOU TELL ME THAT I SOUND LIKE SOME STUPID *NORTHERN PEASANT GIRL* ..."

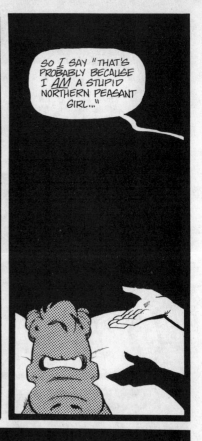

SO *I* SAY "THAT'S PROBABLY BECAUSE I *AM* A STUPID NORTHERN PEASANT GIRL..."

I DON'T KNOW *WHY* YOU CAN'T JUST ADMIT THAT YOU'RE A FAITHFUL FOLLOWER OF THE *EASTERN ORTHODOX CHURCH OF TARIM* AND THEIR BELIEF THAT YOU SHOULD BE A VIRGIN UNTIL YOU'RE *MARRIED*...

I MEAN, EVEN IF YOU *GOT* A DIVORCE, YOU'D STILL WANT TO *YOU-KNOW-WHAT* -- BUT IF YOU DID IT *OUTSIDE* OF MARRIAGE, YOU'D BE BREAKING THE CHURCH LAWS, RIGHT....?

SO WHY NOT JUST MAKE THE BEST OF IT? AT LEAST THIS WAY YOU'RE NOT BREAKING ANY CHURCH LAWS, YOU HAVE ALL THE MONEY AND *BOOZE* YOU WANT AND I HAVE A HUSBAND AND A PLACE TO LIVE AND PEOPLE TO TAKE CARE OF MY *MOTHER*...

end

178

"THE PRESIDENT OF THE UNITED FELDWAR STATES"

HE BELIEVES THAT HE'S ALREADY WON...

ACTS AS IF THIS IS SOME RIDICULOUS SUMMER PAGEANT TO CELEBRATE HIS SELF-DECLARED CORONATION...

THREE POPES DEAD WITHIN A MATTER OF MONTHS -- A CONSENSUS OF CITY-STATES, MONEY PEDDLERS, PARASITES AND MISGUIDED TARIMITES, APPLAUDING HIS EVERY BREATH AND HEART-BEAT ...

AND, IN UPPER FELDA, CIRIN SITS IDLY BY, HER ARMIES WELL-FED, WELL-PAID AND NOWHERE TO BE SEEN...

SHE WISHES -- AND I QUOTE, "TO OBSERVE HIS EXTRAORDINARY METHODS AT SOME LENGTH BEFORE RENDERING A VERDICT ON WHETHER THEY REPRESENT A CLEAR AND IMMINENT DANGER TO OUR CAUSE OF MATERNAL FREEDOM."

ONE RATHER SUPPOSES THAT IF SHE SAW AN ELEPHANT ATTEMPTING TO BALANCE ON ITS TRUNK THAT SHE WOULD RUN UNDERNEATH IT FOR THE SAME REASON...

FLIP

FLUTTER FLUTTER

WEISSHAUPT IS A LARGE, DANGEROUS AND VERY CLUMSY BUFFOON-- MASQUERADING AS A VISIONARY

HE'S OUT OF HIS LEAGUE ALREADY AND HE'S TRYING TO COMPENSATE BY CLIMBING FASTER...

THE TEMPTATION, OF COURSE, IS TO VIEW HIM AS A MOTH, BENT ON SELF-IMMOLATION IN THE CANDLE-FLAME OF POLITICAL EVENTS...

I FEAR, HOWEVER, THAT HE MORE CLOSELY RESEMBLES "

THE ELEPHANT.

end

181

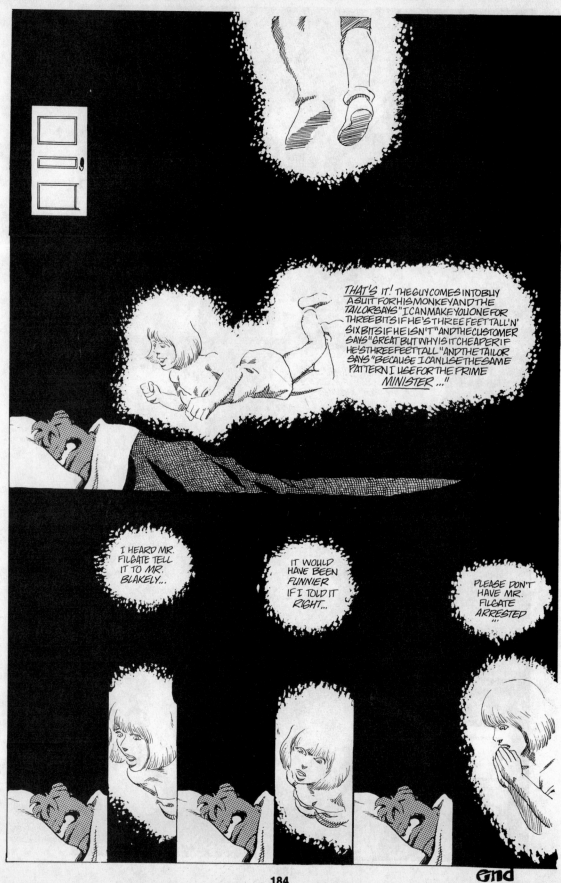

THERESA

OF COURSE, WHEN THE *PRIME MINISTER* RESIGNED AND ASTORIA LEFT, ALL OF THAT CHANGED...

TO BE *PERFECTLY FRANK*, M'SIEU, I FELT *BETRAYED* -- COMPLETELY WITHOUT *RESOURCE* ...

I FLED TO THE *LOWER FELDAN EMBASSY* AND EXPRESSED TO THE *DEPUTY LIASON OFFICER* THE EXTENT OF THE *PITIABLE* SITUATION IN WHICH I FOUND MYSELF...

SMOKE, M'SIEU...?

HE *TOLD* ME

≥*PUFF*≤

HE INSTALLED ME AT HIS ESTATE AS A *GOVERNESS* FOR HIS CHILDREN. FOR A TIME, ALL WAS *PEACEFUL*... AND I FELT *SECURE*

I *THOUGHT* NOT. YOU DON'T SEEM THE *TYPE*.

I WAS A *LOVELY* CHILD AND THAT HE WOULD DO *ALL* WITHIN HIS POWER TO ASSURE MY SAFETY AND THAT I WAS NOT TO WORRY...

THEN HE BEGAN VISITING MY ROOM LATE AT NIGHT. HE WOULD STROKE MY HAIR AND TELL ME I WAS HIS LITTLE FLOWER AND ASK IF I KNEW HOW *FOND* HE WAS OF ME

ONE NIGHT, HE *WEPT* AND TOLD ME HE NO LONGER *LOVED* HIS WIFE AND THAT HE WISHED ME TO BE WITH HIM *ALWAYS*. DESERTION WAS OUT OF THE QUESTION BECAUSE OF HIS *CAREER*.

I TOLD HIM I *COULDN'T* CONSIDER HIS OFFER. AT LEAST NOT WHILE I RESIDED IN HIS WIFE'S HOME. IT WOULDN'T BE... *PROPER*

HE FOUND ME A SPACIOUS APARTMENT FACING ONTO *EMBASSY PARK* AND PROVIDED ME WITH A GENEROUS ALLOWANCE...

HIS VISITS WERE *INFREQUENT* OF COURSE... BECAUSE OF HIS MANY *RESPONSIBILITIES*... AND I FOUND MYSELF WITH A GREAT DEAL OF *SPARE TIME*...

I BEGAN *ENTERTAINING*. SMALL DINNER PARTIES FOR THE CREAM OF *IESTAN SOCIETY*. MY SALONS BECAME WELL-KNOWN AND INVITATIONS WERE MUCH SOUGHT-AFTER BY THE BETTER FAMILIES

MY PATRON *DISAPPROVED* AND ONE DAY HE ARRIVED IN NO FIT STATE TO BE RECEIVED BY A *LADY.* HE INFORMED ME THAT HE INTENDED TO LEAVE HIS WIFE, REGARDLESS OF THE *CONSEQUENCES* AND DEMANDED TO KNOW IF I WOULD AGREE TO *MARRY HIM.*

I TOLD HIM I NEEDED MORE TIME TO CONSIDER IT, AND HE FLEW INTO A *TERRIBLE* RAGE. HIS ACCUSATIONS, ALL *UNFOUNDED* OF COURSE, WERE MOST *UNPLEASANT.* HE CALLED ME VILE NAMES AND TOLD ME HE WAS HAVING ME *EVICTED* AND *CANCELLING* MY ALLOWANCE.

HE SAID HE WOULD SEE ME BEGGING FOR COPPERS IN THE *FISH MARKETS* AND STORMED OUT...

HE RETURNED LATER THAT NIGHT AND THREW *HIM-SELF* AT MY FEET

HE *BEGGED* FOR MY FORGIVENESS. HE HAD BROUGHT THE DEEDS TO HIS LAND IN THE LOWER CITY AND THESE HE PRESSED UPON ME WITH *URGENT ENTREATIES* THAT I NOT *DESPISE HIM...*

WHEN HE LEFT, I SENT THE DEEDS BY *COURIER* TO HIS *WIFE* ALONG WITH A NOTE EXPLAINING ALL THAT HAD *TRANSPIRED* AND ASKING HER HELP IN ENDING HIS *HARASSMENT* OF ME...

EVIDENTLY, SHE INFORMED THE SENIOR OFFICIALS AT THE *EMBASSY* AND THEY TERMINATED HIS POST. I UNDERSTAND SHE HAS SINCE LEFT FOR *NEW SEPRA* TO REJOIN HER FAMILY...

HE CAME ONCE MORE TO MY APARTMENTS AND GAVE ME A CASHIER'S CHEQUE FOR SOME *THREE THOUSAND CROWNS* AND A LETTER OF *INTRO-DUCTION* TO YOU ,.. A *FORGERY,* OF COURSE,... ON THE *PRIME MINISTER'S STATIONERY* ...

HE ASKED ME TO PETITION YOU FOR SOME GOVERNMENT JOB OR OTHER. HE SAID I WAS WELL THOUGHT-OF IN THE HIGHER OFFICES OF THE GOVERNMENT...

HE SAID IF I WOULD JUST DO THIS ONE LAST THING FOR HIM, HE WOULD NEVER BOTHER ME *AGAIN* IN ANY WAY...

I *ACCEPTED* THE MONEY AND THE LETTER, FULLY INTENDING TO REPORT THE MATTER TO THE *FEDERAL COURTS* AND TO, ONCE AND FOR ALL, HAVE DONE WITH HIM...

BUT, THE MORE I *CONSIDERED* IT, THE MORE I *REALISED* THAT IT WAS A RARE OPPORTUNITY THAT I MIGHT BE *FORFEITING* BECAUSE OF MY FOOLISH PRIDE...

A RARE OPPORTUNITY FOR US *BOTH,* M'SIEU ...

I TRUST YOU'LL FORGIVE ME IF I'M *BLUNT* AND TO THE *POINT*...

YOU HAVE BEEN -- AND NO DOUBT WILL *CONTINUE* TO BE -- A BEACON OF LEADERSHIP FOR OUR YOUNG *CONFEDERATION* ...

BUT, IN THE SOCIAL CIRCLES I FREQUENT, YOU HAVE A REPUTATION AS A ... PLEASE FORGIVE ME ... AS A *BOOR* ...

YOU MUST UNDERSTAND THAT THE STANDARDS EXPECTED OF ONE IN YOUR *LOFTY POSITION* ARE EXCEPTIONAL TO SAY THE LEAST...

TRIVIAL CONCERNS TO YOU, NO DOUBT...TOO FEW COURSES AT A *STATE DINNER*...THE WRONG WINE...GARISH DRAPERIES... GROTESQUE SILVERWEAR...

BUT FOR THOSE BRED TO THE ...*FINER THINGS*... THE STAMP IS UNMIS-TAKABLE...

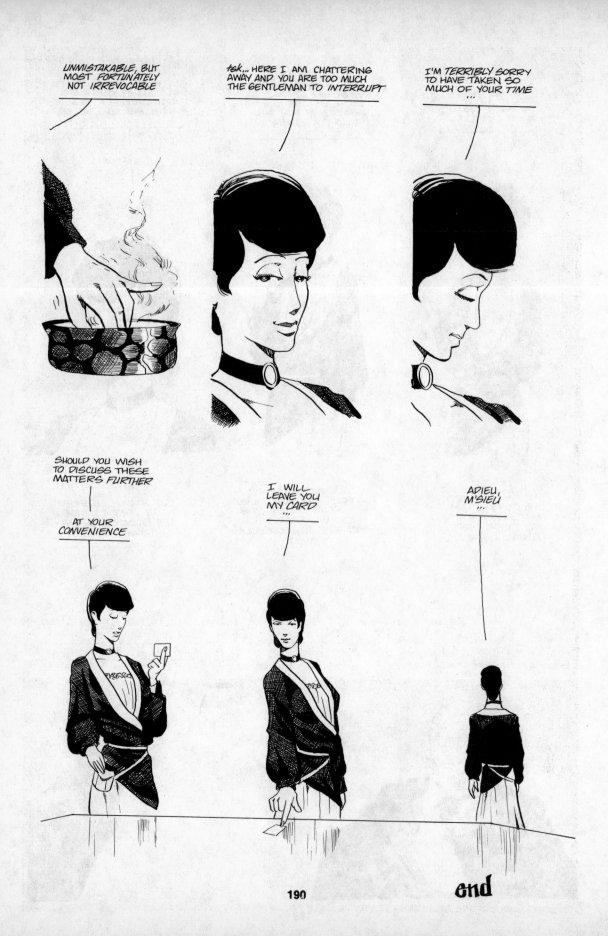

190

end

StORMY WeaTheR

CEREBUS DOESN'T _BELIEVE_ THIS...

CEREBUS WAS asked all the time if

he was the one who was running the government or if he was just a front man for Astoria and her organization. When His Holiness mentioned something to Cerebus a while ago about letting the queens and the priestesses settle things amongst themselves, it made Cerebus think of Astoria. It is very difficult as Prime Minister to figure out if you should listen to the head of the Church that you belong to or to listen to Weisshaupt since he's the one who gave Cerebus back his job.

What is Cerebus supposed to do, anyway? How does someone stop Weisshaupt... what would you stop him with. Cerebus doesn't even know what it is exactly that Weisshaupt is doing, except that everyone is doing what he tells them to do, including Cerebus. If all this has something to do with queens and priestesses, how in Tarim's name is <u>Cerebus</u> going to stop Weisshaupt. Cerebus doesn't even know how the

SOMETHING CEREBUS WAS

always asked was why Astoria was always around when Cerebus was making decisions. This was for a very good reason. Cerebus would often forget what Cerebus was going to do and Astoria would remind him. After a while Cerebus didn't even bother trying to remember what he was doing. A good leader should always have someone around to remember what he is doing so he has time for more important things like

How to stop Weisshaupt

1. Cerebus has to raise his own personal large army

2. Cerebus needs lots and lots of money

196

197

POWERS

YES...

WEISSHAUPT IS WINNING -- AT THE MOMENT. HIS SUCCESS, HOWEVER...

...IS ATTRIBUTABLE PRIMARILY TO OUR INABILITY TO SELECT A SUITABLE CANDIDATE FOR PONTIFF...

HE'S BANKING ON THE FACT THAT I WILL BE PERMITTED ONLY SO MANY FAILURES BEFORE I AM RECALLED TO SERREA...

BANKING ON THE TIME SUCH A MOVE WOULD BUY HIM...

203

204

APPOINTMENTS

SO THAT WAS THE ENVIRONMENT ASTORIA FOUND HERSELF IN FROM EARLY ADOLESCENCE -- THE CHOSEN SUCCESSOR TO *CIRIN*, IN TRAINING TO LEAD THE NEW MATRIARCHY ONE DAY...

SHE WAS NOT UNMINDFUL OF THOSE WITHIN CIRIN'S GOVERNMENT WHO OPPOSED THE DECISION

SHE WAS *CHILDLESS*, YOU SEE. CIRIN SAW HER AS THE EMBODIMENT OF THE *NEW MATRIARCHY* AND FELT THAT THE BIRTH THAT WOULD MAKE ASTORIA A FULL CITIZEN HAD TO BE SPECIAL... HAD TO PLANNED. THE FATHER,...THE HOUR OF CONCEPTION. EVERYTHING...

HER ADVISORS WARNED HER THAT ASTORIA WAS TOO *INDEPENDANT*... SHE ATTRIBUTED THIS TO *JEALOUSY* WHICH WAS ONLY *PARTLY TRUE* ...

IN FACT, BY HER SELECTION, CIRIN HAD PLACED ASTORIA IN A SITUATION THAT WAS UNTENABLE *POLITICALLY*. CIRIN TOLD HER *EVERYTHING* AND ENCOURAGED HER TO PARTICIPATE IN THE SETTING OF POLICY AND THE FRAMING OF THE COUNCIL DEBATES...

THE REST OF THE GOVERNMENT WAS A *LOCKED ROOM* FOR ASTORIA, HOWEVER. AND SHE WAS SOPHISTICATED ENOUGH TO SEE THE WRITING ON THE WALL, THOUGH SHE WAS STILL IN HER TEENS...

CIRIN COULD *ORDER* HER FOLLOWERS TO ACCEPT ASTORIA BUT LIKE *ANY* BUREAUCRACY, THEY COULD MAKE ASTORIA'S LIFE *HELL*, WHILE STILL PRESENTING A *FACADE* OF COOPERATION

SO, SEVERAL WEEKS BEFORE SHE WAS TO MARRY CIRIN'S ADOPTED SON, *SIR GERRIK*, IN A LAVISH STATE CEREMONY, ASTORIA MARRIED HIM IN *PRIVATE*, AND WAS, IN A MATTER OF A FEW DAYS -- IN A *FAMILY WAY.*

SOMETHING WHICH, ACCORDING TO CIRIN'S TIMETABLE, WAS *NOT* TO OCCUR FOR AT *LEAST* THREE MORE YEARS.

WHEN THE COUNCIL TRIED TO MAKE AN ISSUE OF IT, CIRIN EXCUSED IT AS A DIFFERENCE IN PHILOSOPHY -- SHE SUGGESTED THAT ASTORIA'S REBELLION WAS AGAINST THE RIGIDITY OF *CEREMONY* AND THE TRADITIONS OF *FORM*...

SHE MAINTAINED THAT ASTORIA WAS *STEADFAST* IN HER SUPPORT OF THE NEW MATRIARCHY...

HER SPEECH TO THE FULL COUNCIL IN DEFENSE OF HER PROTEGE WAS AN ARTFUL BLEND OF DIPLOMATIC CONCESSIONS AND URGENT PLEAS FOR SUPPORT. CIRIN'S HOLD ON THE GOVERNMENT WAS STILL NEAR TO ABSOLUTE AND THE PROTESTS FOUNDERED ...MOMENTARILY.

THEN, IN HER FINAL MONTH, ASTORIA VANISHED ...

THE OUTCRY RETURNED AND FOR SIX WEEKS, CIRIN STRAINED HER POWERS OF PERSUASION TO THE UTMOST TO MAINTAIN ORDER. FIRST, THERE WAS A PURGE OF THE PREVIOUSLY-TOLERATED OPPOSITION. THEN, A SMALL BORDER WAR WITH LOWER FELDA. SHE FINALLY RESTORED HER CONSENSUS, BUT FOR THE FIRST TIME HER BACKING WAS CONDITIONAL...

IT WAS A VERY COMPLICATED SITUATION. CIRIN WAS VERY MUCH IN CONTROL, BUT SHE HAD ALSO BEEN MADE AWARE THAT SOME MANNER OF *REASONABLE EXPLANATION* WOULD HAVE TO BE FORTH-COMING FROM ASTORIA IF SHE WAS TO CONTINUE WITH FULL SUPPORT FROM HER COUNCIL...

IN THE MIDST OF CIRIN'S JUGGLING THE EXECUTIVE, ASTORIA CAME' BACK...

SHE JUST ARRIVED ONE MORNING IN THE RECEPTION AREA OF CIRIN'S OFFICES AND PATIENTLY WAITED FOR AN AUDIENCE. SHE WAS, OF COURSE, NO LONGER GREAT WITH CHILD...

215

CIRIN'S AIDES WERE DIVIDED ON WHETHER SHE SHOULD MEET WITH ASTORIA... IT WAS, AT LAST, DECIDED THAT AN *INFORMAL* COUNCIL INQUIRY BE HELD THE NEXT MORNING...

MOST OF THE MEMBERS CHOSEN WERE LONG-TIME ALLIES OF CIRIN'S --OR THOSE TRUSTED TO BE IMPARTIAL. CIRIN'S AIM WAS TO MAKE IT THE MILDEST REBUKE POSSIBLE UNDER THE CIRCUMSTANCES

WHICH, HAD ASTORIA CHOSEN TO CO-OPERATE ...

IT MIGHT VERY WELL HAVE *BEEN* ...

AS WITH ALL LEGAL PROCEEDINGS IN UPPER FELDA, ASTORIA WAS ASKED HER STATUS -- *MOTHER OR DAUGHTER* -- A FORMALITY...

ASTORIA TOLD THEM IT WAS NONE OF THEIR BUSINESS ...

THE INQUIRY WAS THROWN INTO A *FRENZY.* CIRIN TURNED SEVERAL SHADES OF CRIMSON

THE COUNCIL SPEAKER WAS THE FIRST TO SENSE THAT THEY WERE WALKING INTO A *TRAP* ...

SHE MOVED FOR A RECESS

CIRIN TOLD HER THERE WAS NO NEED FOR A RECESS -- THEY HADN'T EVEN *GOT* TO THE *DIFFICULT* QUESTIONS YET...

SHE REPHRASED THE *QUESTION*... *HAD* ASTORIA GIVEN BIRTH AND *WAS* THE BABY *ALIVE*?

ASTORIA PLAYED HER TRUMP CARD. SHE SAID SHE PERSONALLY BELIEVED THAT THE LAWS OF THE STATE DID NOT APPLY TO THE RELATIONSHIP BETWEEN A MOTHER AND HER CHILD. SHE WOULD NEITHER *CONFIRM* NOR *DENY* THE BIRTH

A CHILD, ASTORIA SAID, WAS THE *PROPERTY* OF ITS MOTHER, TO DO WITH AS SHE SEES FIT...

ONLY ITS MOTHER COULD DECIDE WHETHER A CHILD SHOULD *LIVE*

OR *DIE.*

IT WAS THEN THAT CIRIN REALIZED THE *EXTENT* OF THE DILEMMA SHE FACED.

SEVERAL INQUIRY BOARD MEMBERS URGED EXECUTION ...BUT ON WHAT *CHARGE* BECAME THE QUESTION...

IF CIRIN GAVE THE ORDER AND IT HAD BEEN A LIVE BIRTH, SHE WOULD BE GUILTY OF A NEARLY *UNIMAGINEABLE* HERESY ...

THE KILLING OF A *MOTHER*

EVEN A STILL BIRTH WOULD ONLY MEAN ASTORIA WASN'T YET A CITIZEN...

THE KEY WAS THE VIEWPOINT SHE HAD EXPRESSED THAT THE COUNCIL HAD NO BUSINESS IN THE RELATIONSHIP BETWEEN A MOTHER AND CHILD...

CIRIN GOT THE COUNCIL TO AGREE THAT SO LONG AS NO EVIDENCE EXISTED OF INFANTICIDE, ASTORIA COULD NOT BE EXECUTED...

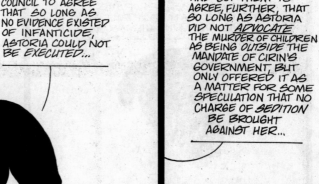

AND GOT THEM TO AGREE, FURTHER, THAT SO LONG AS ASTORIA DID NOT *ADVOCATE* THE MURDER OF CHILDREN AS BEING *OUTSIDE* THE MANDATE OF CIRIN'S GOVERNMENT, BUT ONLY OFFERED IT AS A MATTER FOR SOME SPECULATION THAT NO CHARGE OF *SEDITION* BE BROUGHT AGAINST HER...

THE PROCESS WAS A GOOD DEAL MORE ARDUOUS THAN THAT, OF COURSE, BUT THAT WAS THE COMPROMISE REACHED. CIRIN HAD ALIENATED MUCH OF HER CONSTITUENCY, BUT ASTORIA WAS NOW SAFE FROM PROSECUTION...

UNTIL THE JUDGEMENT WAS READ -- AND IT WAS ASTORIA WHO OBJECTED. SHE *WAS* ADVOCATING THE MURDER OF CHILDREN BY THEIR MOTHERS AS BEING OUTSIDE THE MANDATE OF CIRIN'S GOVERNMENT -- OR ANY GOVERNMENT...

IT WAS A PERSONAL CONVICTION, SHE SAID. HER BELIEFS WERE SUCH THAT SHE FELT EACH INDIVIDUAL SHOULD ADVOCATE *ALL* OF THEIR OWN ATTITUDES RATHER THAN ADVOCATING THE BELIEFS OF THE SOCIETY OR GOVERNING STRUCTURE IN WHICH THEY FIND THEMSELVES

IT WAS THE SHEN DEVOTIONAL BELIEFS -- THE 'KEVIL'. TYPICALLY, ASTORIA HAD TAKEN A SYSTEM OF MEDITATION AND MADE IT INTO A POLITICAL MOVEMENT. THE NEXT MORNING...

MR. PRESIDENT -- STATE LEADERS JULIUS AND LEONARDI ARE HERE

GOODNESS -- I'VE TAKEN UP SO MUCH OF YOUR TIME WITH MY *BABBLING* ONCE AGAIN...

NO -- PLEASE GO ON

"THE NEXT MORNING..."

222

224

227

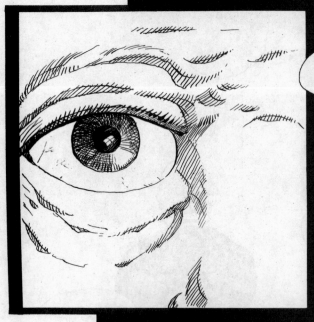

MIND GAME IV

CEREBUS WANTS AN ALE...

THERE *ISN'T* ANY ALE. HANEK TOLD CEREBUS HIMSELF "

THE ALE WON'T BE IN FOR THREE MORE DAYS...

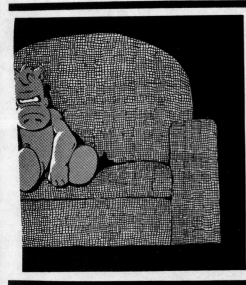

LOUSY HOTEL. CEREBUS WANTS A *WHISKEY*, THEN.

WHISKEY GIVES CEREBUS THE *RUNS* ...

CEREBUS WON'T DRINK THAT *MUCH* ...

CEREBUS ALWAYS SAYS HE WON'T DRINK THAT MUCH, BUT CEREBUS ALWAYS *DOES* ...

CEREBUS WILL ORDER *TWO SMALL GLASSES* ...THE ONES THAT THEY BRING THE *ORANGE JUICE* IN ...

THEY ALWAYS BRING THE BOTTLE AND CEREBUS ALWAYS TELLS THEM TO LEAVE IT ...

CEREBUS DOESN'T *ALWAYS* TELL THEM TO LEAVE IT ...

NO. SOMETIMES CEREBUS JUST ORDERS A *REFILL* EVERY TWO MINUTES UNTIL THEY GET THE HINT AND LEAVE IT WITHOUT BEING *ASKED* ...

CEREBUS IS ONLY GOING TO DRINK UNTIL THE RIGHT SIDE OF HIS *GUT* STARTS TO *HURT*...

...AND THEN CEREBUS WILL DRINK FASTER TO KILL THE *PAIN*.

LIKE THAT TIME CEREBUS ALMOST *DIED* IN TANSUBAL...

CEREBUS QUIT DRINKING THAT TIME...

FOR AN *AFTERNOON.*

ALMOST A *WHOLE DAY.*

ONLY BECAUSE CEREBUS PASSED OUT AT DUSK AND DIDN'T WAKE UP 'TIL *NOON*...

ONE DRINK.

UNCLE ERIC DIED OF IT...

IT WAS BETTER THAN LIVING WITH *AUNT ROSE.*

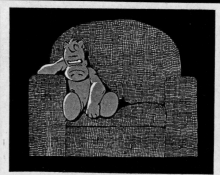

TRUE ENOUGH.

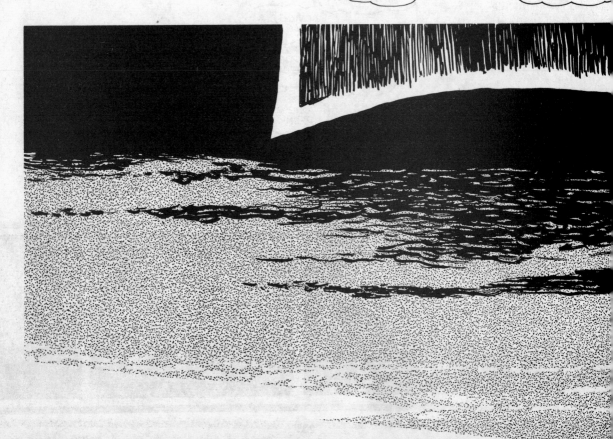

234

JOIN UP WITH AN *ARMY*. PUT SOME FOP CITY TO THE TORCH AND LIVE LIKE A *KING* OFF THE PLUNDER ...

NEVER GETTING *PAID*.

AYE. THE ARMY.

LOSING.

CEREBUS GOT AN URN FULL OF GOLD THAT ONE TIME...

BUT CEREBUS LOST IT OFF THE PIER WHEN HE WAS BUYING THAT *BOAT*...

MARCHING, WADING, CLIMBING, STARVING, FREEZING

BUT, IF IT HADN'T TIPPED OVER, CEREBUS COULD HAVE LIVED LIKE A *KING*...

CEREBUS WOULD HAVE GONE TO THE NEAREST TAVERN AND LOST IT ALL PLAYING *DIAMONDBACK*...

AYE. FORGET MONEY. WHAT CEREBUS NEEDS IS A GOOD FIGHT.

AYE. A FIGHT.

THEY'RE ALWAYS TAKING ADVANTAGE OF CEREBUS' GOOD NATURE...

BASTARDS.

AND THEY TALK ABOUT CEREBUS BEHIND HIS BACK. CEREBUS KNOWS.

CEREBUS SEES THEM LAUGHING. CEREBUS IS KEEPING A LIST IN HIS HEAD.

THEY'LL PAY...

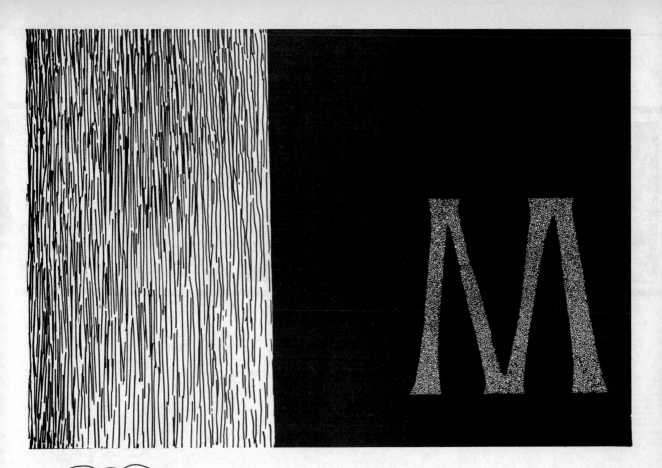

GET ONE OF THOSE DOUBLE-EDGED TWO-HANDER'S FOR THE NEXT CABINET MEETING...

STATE, FINANCE, TREASURY AND TRANSPORT SHISH KEBOB...

"STOP WEISSHAUPT" CEREBUS SHOULD JUST DROP HIM OFF THE WALL INTO THE LOWER CITY...

LET THE PEASANTS AND LIVESTOCK GNAW ON THE OLD LARDBUCKET'S CARCASS A WHILE...

FORCE-FEED 'IM THE BUSINESS END OF A SHORT SWORD AND WATCH HIS EYEBALLS SWELL

MAYBE JUST GET THE OLD THUMBS UNDER ONE OF HIS CHINS AND...

WHERE'S CEREBUS' DAMN WHISKEY?!

A FEW BUCKETS OF OIL AND A COUPLE OF TORCHES...

REDUCE THE WHOLE DAMN REGENCY TO A PILE OF OVER-PRICED ASHES

MAYBE JUST BREAK EVERYONE'S LEGS AND WATCH THEM WIGGLE AROUND THE...

WHERE'S CEREBUS' DAMN ...

SORRY ≶PANT≶ SIR. I ≶PUFF≶ HAD TO ≶PANT≶ GO DOWN ≶PUFF≶ THE HALL TO GET IT...

WOULD YOU ≶PANT≶ LIKE A GLASS, SIR

YES.　NO.

YES.　NO.

ONLY STUPID NORTHERN PEASANTS DRINK OUT OF THE BOTTLE.

CEREBUS
IS A STUPID
NORTHERN
PEASANT.

GULP

NO GLASS.

VERY GOOD, SIR.

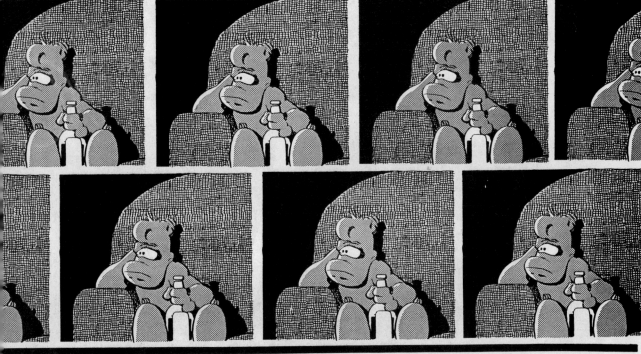

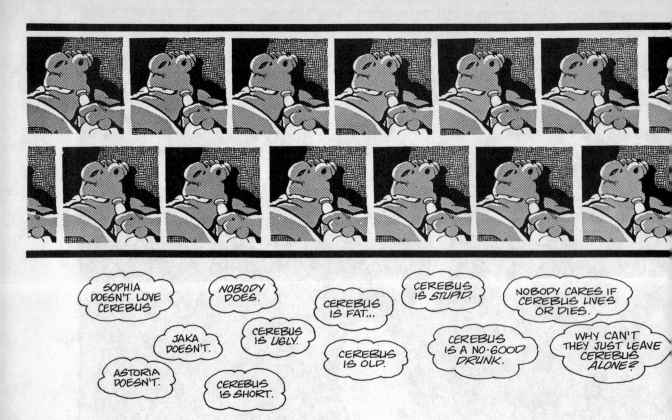

SOPHIA DOESN'T LOVE CEREBUS

NOBODY DOES.

CEREBUS IS FAT...

CEREBUS IS *STUPID*.

NOBODY CARES IF CEREBUS LIVES OR DIES.

JAKA DOESN'T.

CEREBUS IS UGLY.

CEREBUS IS OLD.

CEREBUS IS A NO-GOOD *DRUNK*.

WHY CAN'T THEY JUST LEAVE CEREBUS *ALONE?*

ASTORIA DOESN'T.

CEREBUS IS SHORT.

GULP

WEISSHAUPT... WISE HOP......... WISE GUY HOT

CEREBUS THE HANDPUPPET

PRESIDENT WIGGY-PIGGY

PRIME MINISTER WHISKEY-PISKEY

FIRST YOU WHISKEY .....THEN YOU PISKEY.

MORE WHISKEY-PISKEY.

NO. NO MORE WHISKEY.

CEREBUS' GUT HURTS

CEREBUS' EYES HURT

CEREBUS' HEAD HURTS

CEREBUS CAN'T SEE STRAIGHT.

CEREBUS JUST HAS TO SIT STILL ...

BREATHE IN AND OUT...

RELAX RELAX RELAX

CEREBUS HAS THE SHAKES ...

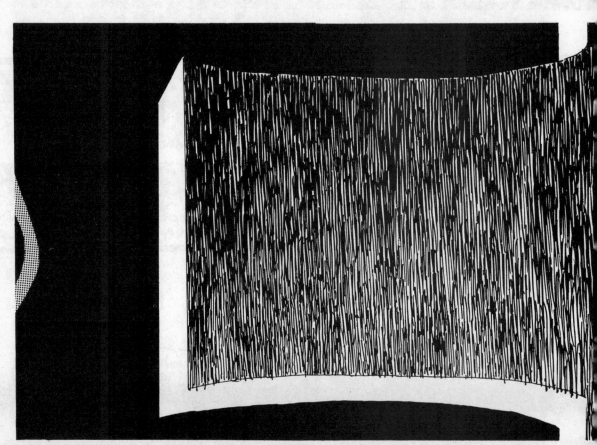

IT'S JUST CEREBUS' NERVES.

CEREBUS IS UNDER A LOT OF PRESSURE

PEOPLE LAUGHING AT HIM.

EVERYONE HATES CEREBUS

CEREBUS DOESN'T CARE...

CEREBUS JUST NEEDS SOMETHING TO STEADY HIS NERVES

ONE LITTLE DRINK.

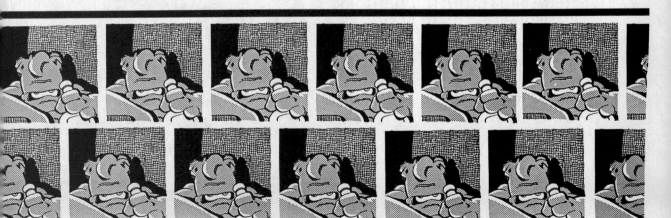

JUST ONE.

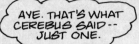 AYE. THAT'S WHAT CEREBUS SAID -- JUST ONE.

 OKAY.

 OKAY.

GULP GULP GULP GU

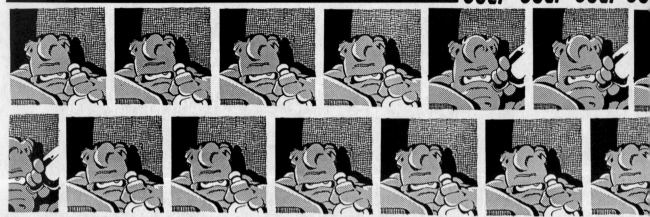

OKAY. THAT'S ENOUGH.

CEREBUS FEELS *STEADIER* NOW.

BUT CEREBUS' HEAD STILL HURTS.

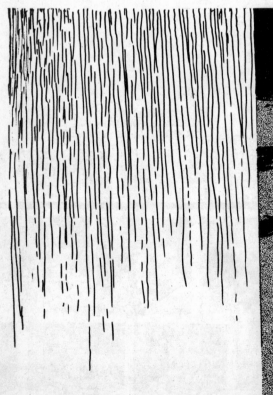

 JUST ONE MORE...

 THEN CEREBUS WILL HAVE A CLEAR HEAD TO GO WITH HIS STEADY NERVES.

 THEN CEREBUS CAN MAKE SOME PLANS.

 CEREBUS CAN'T MAKE PLANS WHEN CEREBUS' HEAD HURTS,...

 TRUE.

GULP GULP

 CEREBUS WILL JUST DRINK UNTIL HIS HEAD DOESN'T HURT ANYMORE AND STOP

 GOOD.

 GOOD.

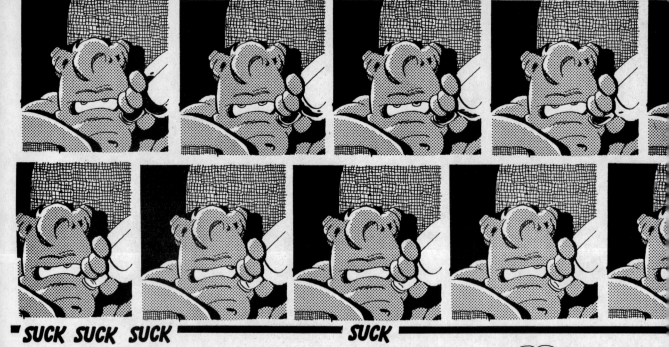

EMPTY. ALONE.

AND CEREBUS' HEAD WAS JUST ABOUT TO STOP HURTING

ANOTHER BOTTLE

NO.

CEREBUS' GUT HURTS TOO MUCH...

CEREBUS' EYES HURT ...

CEREBUS' LEG IS ASLEEP

CEREBUS CAN'T SEE STRAIGHT...

BOOK THREE
Church and State

255

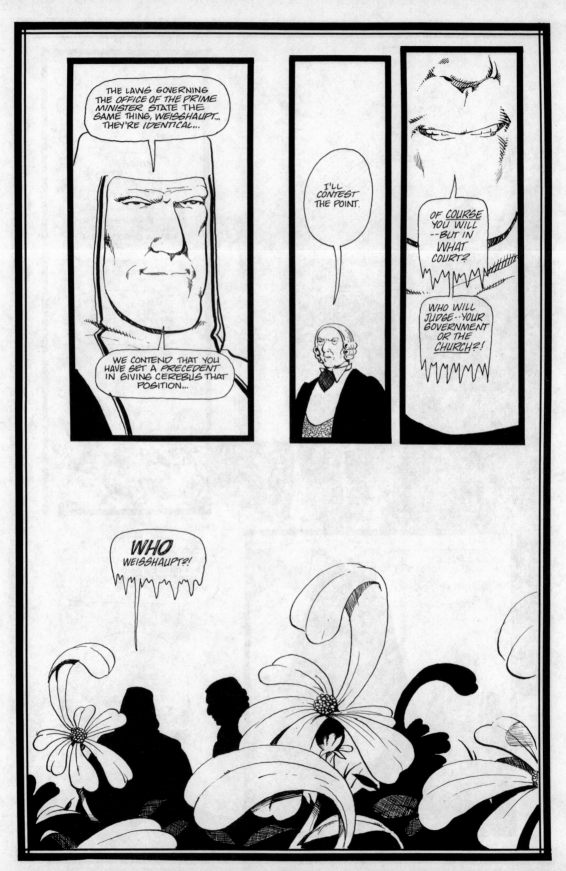

THE LAWS GOVERNING THE OFFICE OF THE PRIME MINISTER STATE THE SAME THING, WEISSHAUPT... THEY'RE IDENTICAL...

WE CONTEND THAT YOU HAVE SET A PRECEDENT IN GIVING CEREBUS THAT POSITION...

I'LL CONTEST THE POINT.

OF COURSE YOU WILL --BUT IN WHAT COURT?

WHO WILL JUDGE--YOUR GOVERNMENT OR THE CHURCH?!

WHO WEISSHAUPT?!

258

WELL, IF YOU ASK *ME*, I THINK IT'S *WONDERFUL* NEWS...

I MEAN, YOU'RE *AL*WAYS COM*PLAIN*ING THAT YOU'RE NOTHING MORE THAN WEISSHAUPT'S *PUPPET* *AREN'T* YOU?

WELL, HE DOESN'T HAVE ANY CONTROL OVER THE CHURCH AT *ALL*...

YOU'LL *FIN*ALLY BE ABLE TO DECIDE WHAT YOU WANT TO *DO* AND THEN YOU CAN *DO* IT

CEREBUS DOESN'T...

"..WANT TO DO *ANYTHING.*" I KNOW, I *KNOW*

BUT IF YOU DON'T *WANT* TO DO ANYTHING, WHY DO YOU HATE BEING PRIME MINISTER SO MUCH?

YOU TOLD CEREBUS THAT LAST *NIGHT*...

I MUST SAY I COULDN'T BE MORE *PLEASED*

YOU SAID *THAT* LAST NIGHT, TOO...

I'LL HAVE YOUR LIQUOR SMUGGLED IN FOR YOU... AND, OF COURSE, I'LL LET YOU KNOW IF THERE'S ANYTHING I WANT APPROVED BY THE *CHURCH*

YOU SAID *THAT* THIS MORNING ...

YES.

OF COURSE.

I JUST DON'T WANT YOU TO BE WORRIED THAT I WON'T BE HERE TO *HELP* YOU ...

CEREBUS ISN'T WORRIED...

WE HAVE AN UNDERSTANDING, THEN?

GOOD. GOOD.

WELL, THEN. IF YOU FIND YOU NEED ANY KIND OF...

CEREBUS WILL SEND A MESSAGE TO YOUR OFFICE...

YOU TOLD CEREBUS THAT LAST NIGHT *AND* THIS MORNING...

EVIDENTLY, SOMEONE IS ON THEIR WAY WITH YOUR ROBES. IF YOU'D LIKE ME TO *STAY*...

CEREBUS CAN GET DRESSED BY *HIMSELF*.

272

ANY
THING
DONE
FOR
the FIRST
TIME
unleashes
a demon

273

274

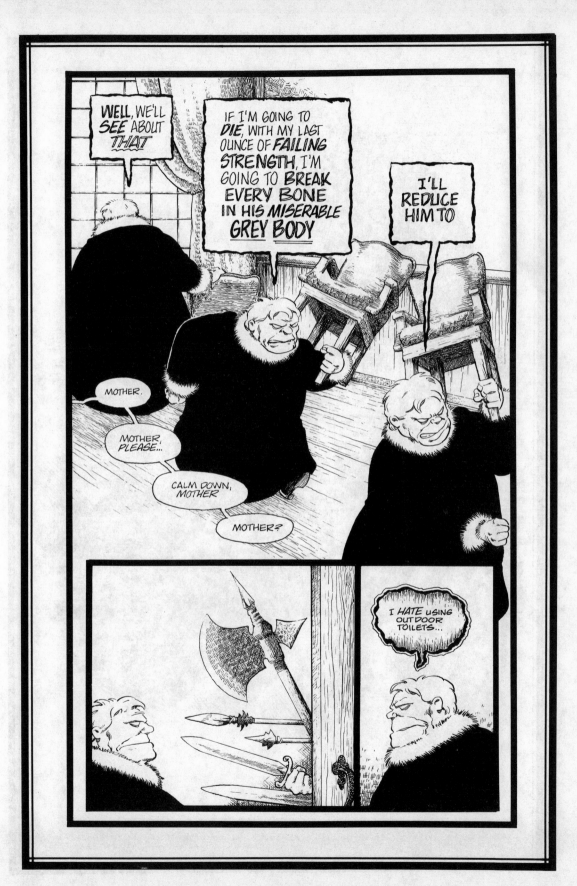

279

283

MOST HOLY HAS A LOT OF HARD WORK AHEAD OF HIM, POSEY

MOST HOLY IS GOING TO GET THE WESTERN CHURCH OUT OF THIS CITY...

TO DO THAT, MOST HOLY IS GOING TO NEED THE SUPPORT OF HIS PEOPLE-- DO YOU KNOW WHO MOST HOLY'S PEOPLE ARE, POSEY?

THE POOR AND THE DISENFRANCHISED?

EVERYONE WHO THINKS MOST HOLY IS PERFECT AND WHO WILL OBEY HIS EVERY COMMAND WITHOUT QUESTION...

MAKE SENSE, POSEY. YOU CAN'T CONQUER SQUAT WITH THE POOR AND DISENFRANCHISED.

285

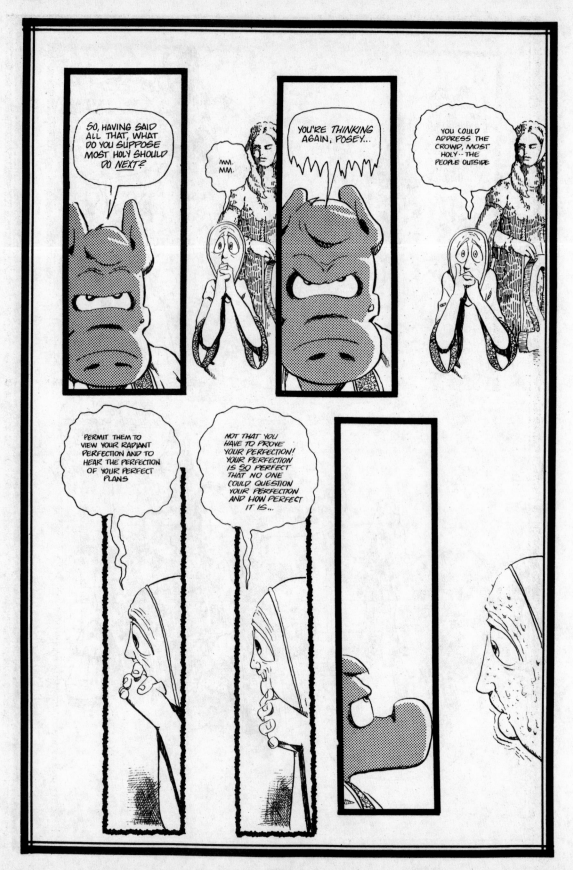

286

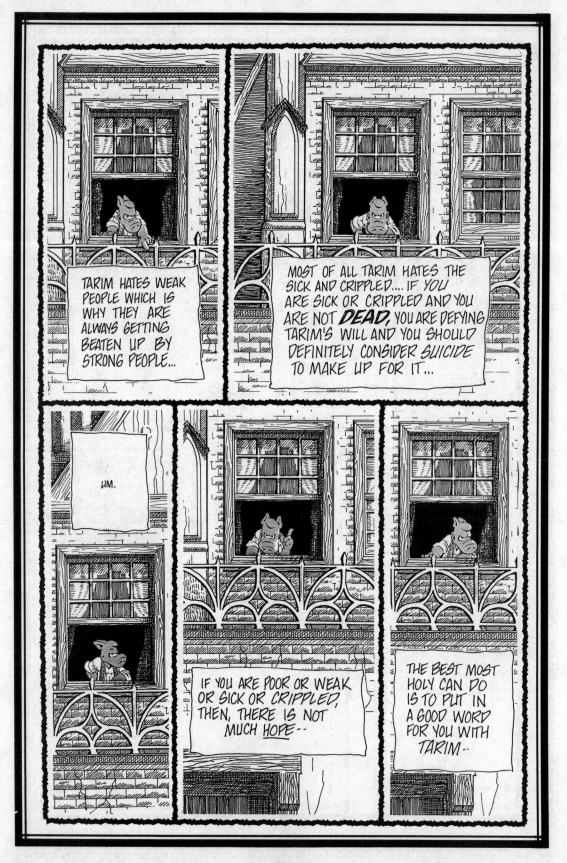

Next **QUESTIONS and ANSWERS**

THE THRILL of agony AND the VICTORY of defeat

BACKGROUNDS BY GERHARD

294

296

302

303

305

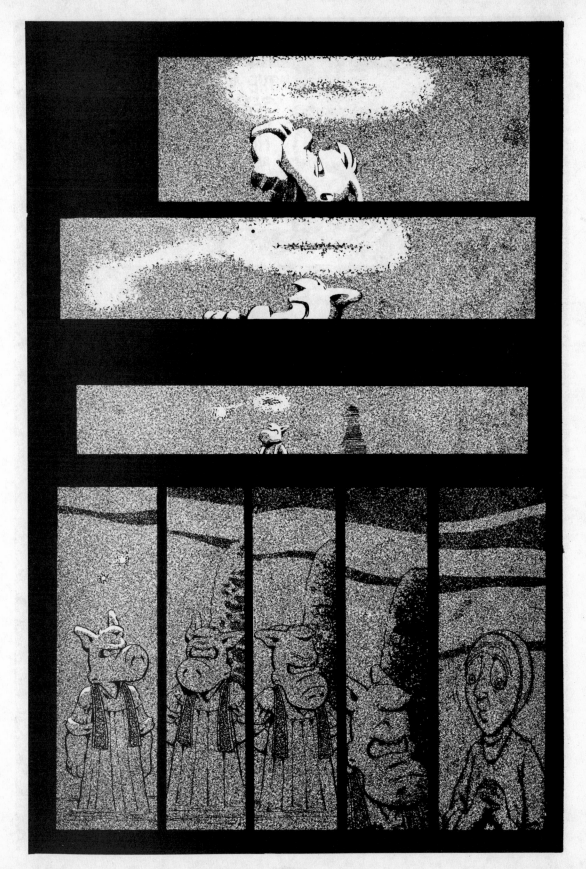

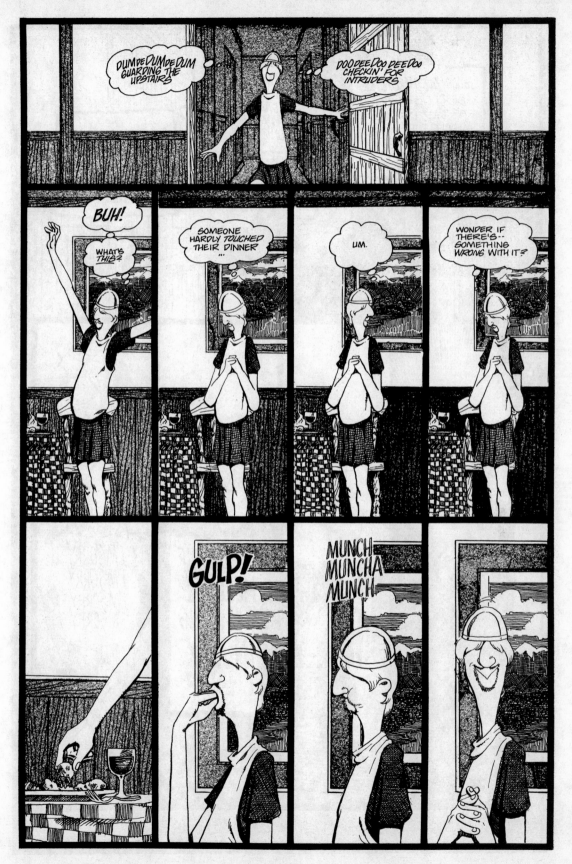

309

311

NEXT

Where he's been and what he's been up to

DAY OF GREATNESS

Note: Remind Most Holy - Fret Mac Mury - not of eternity - honey - nostrils - soldier ants

betrayed Most Holy back in the days when Most Holy wasn't yet officially perfect. Most Holy counted on you and you let Most Holy down. You never came back with the Pigt armies and Most Holy had to resign as Prime Minister and everyone laughed at Most Holy. Before Most Holy decides what he wants to fill your intestines with for the rest of eternity, is there anything you want to tell Most Holy?

Muffins: I told your people that you needed them, Great Cerebus. I told them that the time of Re-emergence was at hand, but Fret Mac Mury had convinced them all in my absence that you were a false Cerebus.

Most Holy: It doesn't matter. Most Holy doesn't need them. Most Holy has his own plan. Most Holy is going to get all of the gold coins in the world and then Most Holy is going to buy all of the best mercenary armies in the world and then Most Holy is going to send them out to conquer everything and have everyone who doesn't believe Most Holy is perfect put to death.

Muffins: A wonderful plan. A perfect plan.

Most Holy: You think Most Holy is crazy.

Muffins: No, Great Cerebus. No. No.

Most Holy: Most Holy talks about capturing everything and you don't think Most Holy is crazy?

AGE OF CONSENT

313

Muffins: How can you be, Great Cerebus? You've said yourself that you're perfect. Our legends speak of your Great Dream.

Most Holy: Cerebus had a dream last night. Cerebus was flying over this body of water and there were these doors all around him, just sort of floating above the water. Up ahead, Cerebus could see this stone column sticking up out of the water and Cerebus flew toward it. When Cerebus got to it, the water had risen almost to the top. There was this stone post and on the post was a box and in the box was a crown. Cerebus tried to grab the crown but a gust of wind came up and blew Cerebus away. Then Cerebus was blown against this big glass door and it broke and Cerebus was stuck. Then the glass door started floating back towards the stone column which turned into a statue of Cerebus. Cerebus kept trying to get out, but he was stuck. As Cerebus got closer to the statue, it started to crumble to pieces. Cerebus thought he was either going to be crushed by one of the falling chunks or squeezed against the statue's forehead.
Muffins: And what happened, Great Cerebus?
Most Holy: Cerebus woke up with a craving for raw potatoes and onion soup.

Muffins: It's a wonderful dream; a perfect dream.
Most Holy: Most Holy was just testing you when he asked if you thought he was crazy.
Muffins: Of course, Great Cerebus.
Most Holy: Most Holy would've had your head cut off and made into a footstool if you had said he was.
Muffins: I understand, Great Cerebus.
Most Holy: Most Holy doesn't want to talk to you anymore, so go away. If Most Holy wants to talk to you again, Most Holy will send Bear to get you.

Muffins: Yes, Great Cerebus, and what do you wish me to
do while I am gone?
Most Holy: Nothing. Just sit in a chair somewhere.
You can breathe if you have to.
Muffins: "And his mercy will ~~know~~ no bounds"

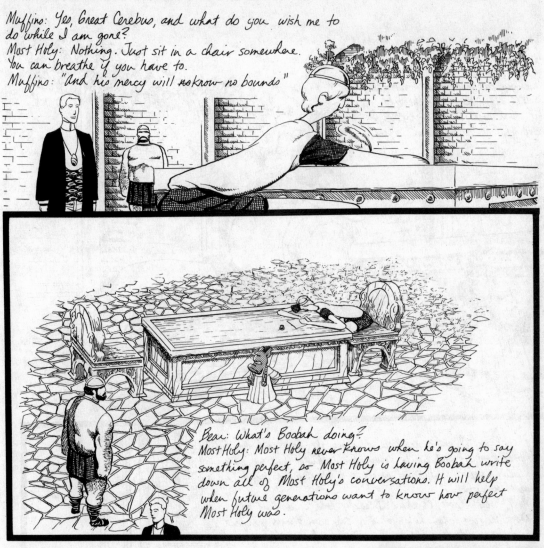

Bear: What's Boobah doing?
Most Holy: Most Holy never knows when he's going to say
something perfect, so Most Holy is having Boobah write
down all of Most Holy's conversations. It will help
when future generations want to know how perfect
Most Holy was.

Besides it seemed like the easiest way to keep Boobah out of

BUMP

315

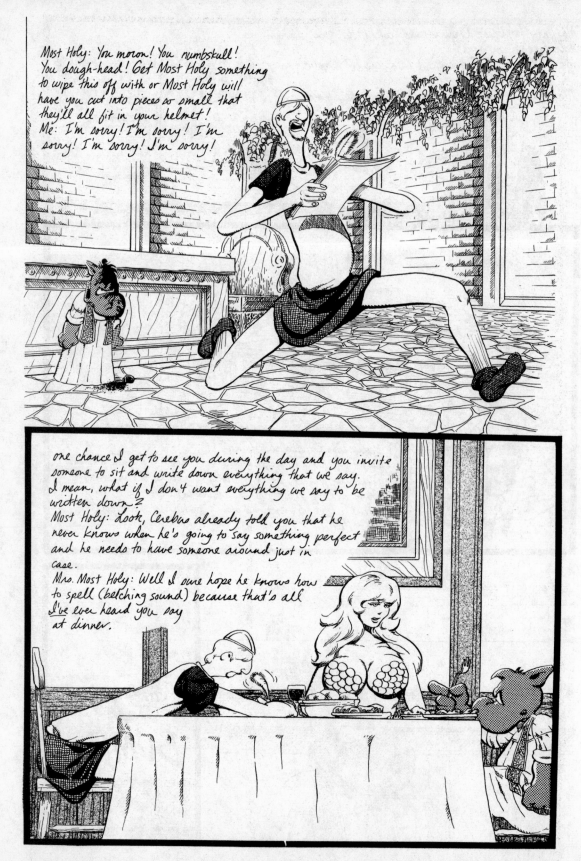

Most Holy: You moron! You numbskull!
You dough-head! Get Most Holy something
to wipe this off with or Most Holy will
have you cut into pieces so small that
they'll all fit in your helmet!
Me: I'm sorry! I'm sorry! I'm
sorry! I'm sorry! I'm sorry!

one chance I get to see you during the day and you invite
someone to sit and write down everything that we say.
I mean, what if I don't want everything we say to be
written down?
Most Holy: Look, Cerebus already told you that he
never knows when he's going to say something perfect
and he needs to have someone around just in
case.
Mrs. Most Holy: Well I sure hope he knows how
to spell (belching sound) because that's all
I've ever heard you say
at dinner.

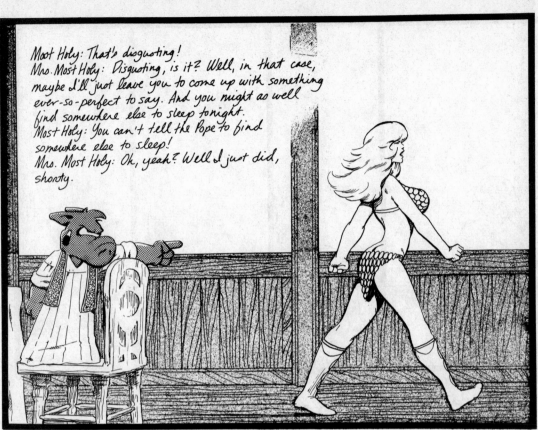

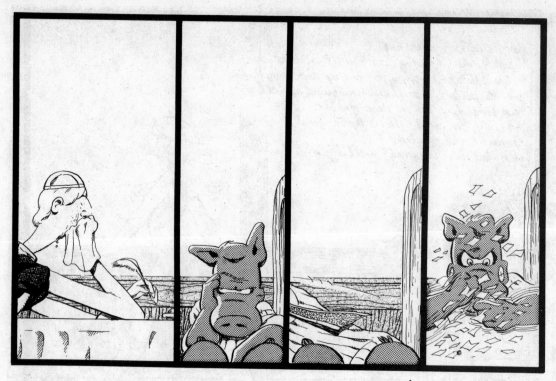

and then Mrs. Most Holy says: "I'm so lucky that a busy Pope like Most Holy always makes sure that he comes upstairs to have dinner with me even though I don't have a gold crown to my name and I haven't the faintest idea of how to help him conquer everything." And then Most Holy says, "Most Holy can't understand why Mrs. Most Holy can't just do as she's told and stop giving Most Holy such a hard time all the damn time. And Mrs. Most Holy says, "Especially when you consider that Most Holy doesn't charge my ugly dried up old prune of a mother a half-bit towards her keep. I mean, she eats like a horse and she snores so loud it keeps Most Holy awake almost every damn night." And then Most Holy says, "If Most Holy wasn't perfect, he probably would have dropped both of you into the Lower City weeks ago." And Mrs. Most Holy says, "Most Holy should do it: at least he wouldn't have to listen to the two of us whine all

Most Holy: Ah, this is more like it. It took Most Holy a while, but he finally figured out what was wrong. It's hard to say perfect things when you're having conversations with imperfect people. Up here on the roof, Most Holy is much closer to Tarim and Most Holy can just say all of the perfect things that come into Most Holy's head.

319

I *TOLD* YOU IT WAS A MISTAKE--COUNTING ON WEISSHAUPT TO KEEP *CONTROL*

I *KNEW* HE WOULD UNDERESTIMATE CEREBUS SOONER OR LATER AND NOW HE HAS...

CEREBUS HAS A ONE-TRACK MIND.

WE CAN EXPECT A *PAPAL CRUSADE* TO BE LAUNCHED AGAINST THE *SEPRAN EMPIRE* ANY TIME NOW...

WE HAVE DONE ALL THAT WE CAN--WE MUST TRUST TO THE *GREAT MOTHER* TO DELIVER US.

ON THE *CONTRARY,* WE HAVEN'T DONE *ANYTHING* BUT SIT ON OUR HANDS-- YOU *COULD* HAVE USED YOUR INFLUENCE WITH CIRIN

WE COULD'VE NIPPED THIS *UNITED FELDWAR STATES* THING IN THE BUD...

BUT YOU SAW A CHANCE TO UNDERMINE CIRIN-- A CHANCE TO BE WEISSHAUPT'S ...

AS *USUAL,* YOU EXAGGERATE TERRIBLY, *ASTORIA.* WE HAVE ALWAYS SETTLED OUR OWN AFFAIRS IN *IEST.*

YOU'VE GOT A POPE FROM *TERIM-ONLY-KNOWS-WHERE* IN THE NORTH, *NO* PRIME MINISTER, AN OCCUPYING FORCE OF *SEPRANS* AND A PRESIDENT FROM *LOWER FELDA...*

IF *THAT'S* WHAT YOU CALL SETTLING YOUR OWN AFFAIRS IN *IEST...*

AND, *INSTEAD*, I SUPPOSE YOU THINK WE SHOULD HAND EVERYTHING OVER TO *YOU*, AGAIN...

...YOU *HAD* YOUR CHANCE, *ASTORIA*. IN FACT, YOU HAVE HAD *SEVERAL* CHANCES

AND I CAME CLOSER TO *LEGITIMIZING* CIRIN'S CAUSE IN THIS CITY-STATE THAN THE LAST THREE RESIDENTS OF *GOODABBEY* PUT *TOGETHER*

THAT YOU DID. THAT YOU DID.

AMID GREAT *ASSURANCES*, AS I RECALL, THAT THE AARDVARK COULDN'T-- HOW DID YOU PUT IT? COULDN'T TAKE A *BREATH* WITHOUT CONSULTING YOU...

IT WOULD SEEM THAT THE PRESIDENT WASN'T ALONE IN UNDERESTIMATING OUR LITTLE GREY FRIEND...

WOULDN'T YOU SAY? HMM?

Mr. Tucker: Thank you for waiting, Mr. President. I have just returned from a meeting on the third floor with Mr. Colin-Hampton who is, as I'm sure you are well aware, the President of the Bank of Iest. He wanted me to assure you that, while it is true that the artificially-created demand for gold coins and our inability to keep up with it has put us in a very vulnerable position, we are working to insure that these problems are solved with all possible haste and common sense.

It is in light of this, that I am able to...

324

When I left Mr. Colin Hampton, he was in conference with the brightest and most efficient of our experts in these matters. I can assure that, even as we speak, they are in the process of formulating a series of suitable responses to the situation at hand and that they have assured me every effort is being made to recommend to Mr. Colin-Hampton a course of action to restore order. Mr. Colin Hampton has assured me, personally, that he is preparing to take the next step.

Most Holy: The day is almost over and we've only taken in six thousand gold coins! Most Holy is disgusted and Tarim will be, too when Most Holy tells him.
Posey: Perhaps, hum hum, you could tell him how generous everyone has been up until now. Perhaps
Most Holy: Perhaps nothing! Most Holy isn't going to lie to Tarim just to get a bunch of peasants off the hook. There are more gold coins out there than this. Most Holy can almost smell all the gold people are hiding

Posey: But, hum hum, they have to eat.
Most Holy: Sure, eat so they can stay alive long enough to have to eat again. They must think that food grows on trees.
Posey: Uh...
Most Holy: No, Most Holy will just have to prove to them that Most Holy is serious about destroying the world unless Most Holy gets enough gold coins.
Posey: Uh...

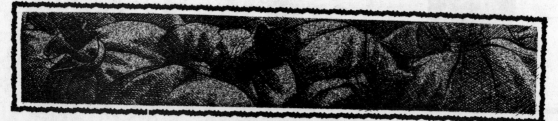

Most Holy: You think Most Holy stands up here shouting just to hear himself shout? Do you? Well, you're wrong. Most Holy is trying to get it through your thick skulls that Tarim isn't kidding. Unless you find Tarim a lot more gold coins, everything is going to be reduced to little piles of ashes. Is that what you want? Is it?

Most Holy: Most Holy knows what you're going to say. You're going to say, "But, Most Holy, we are poor and starving and wretched and we are better off dead".

This is true.

But what Most Holy didn't tell you is that Tarim isn't destroying the world to be a nice guy. Tarim is going to destroy the world because all of you are so worthless that he wants to show you what real suffering is.

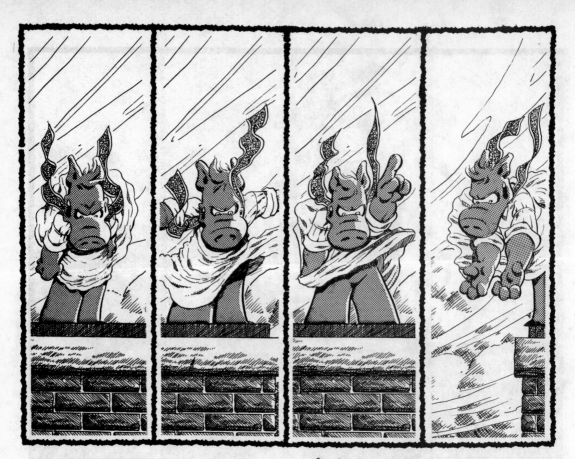

Most Holy: You think you're suffering now? Do you? Well suppose Most Holy were to tell you that when Tarim destroys the world by fire, the first thing to burn is everyone's nostril hair. That's right! Nostril hair!

So when your sinuses start filling up with thick black smoke that smells like burning hair, and the smoke starts billowing out of your tear ducts you'll realize that you had things pretty easy up until then

But then it will be too late. You'll come to Most Holy with your noses melted and your foreheads black, begging him to take your gold coins. And even before Most Holy can tell you, "It's too late; the whole thing is out of Most Holy's hands", Fwoosh, it will be your tongue's turn.

In the blinking of an eye, your molars will be hot enough to fry an egg. Before you can say "I wish hadn't been so stupid", you'll be able to use your tonsils as a night-light. From there it will spread to your stomach. In minutes you'll be a walking liver and kidney stew.

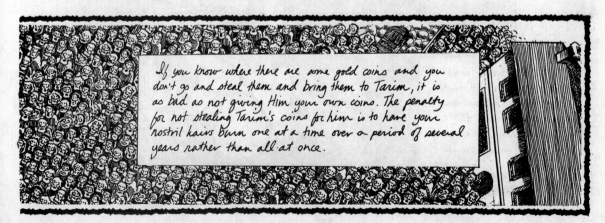

If you know where there are some gold coins and you don't go and steal them and bring them to Tarim, it is as bad as not giving Him your own coins. The penalty for not stealing Tarim's coins for him is to have your nostril hairs burn one at a time over a period of several years rather than all at once.

Most Holy: You still have ten days to locate all of Most Holy's gold and bring it to him. Remember! The first people to ignite will be your children and any other relative that you like a lot.

Ten days. Most Holy has spoken.

Most Holy: Did you get all that, Boobah? Me: Yup.

Most Holy: Well, maybe they're finally getting the right idea. Go out and get some more of those burlap sacks. We're going to need them by tonight

Tomorrow, Most Holy is going to get even more than....

Most Holy: Look, Most Holy knows what you're doing here and you might as well go back to the Red Marches. Cerebus doesn't need any advisors or aides or assistants or cabinet ministers or Co-Popes or anything like that. So go away and...

Muffins: Ok, but Great Cerebus. I'm not here to advise or assist you. No one could do that. I am simply here to observe the miracle as it occurs.

Yeah?

You observe anything yet?

I picked up a discarded letter written by a young girl in the Lower City. I also have a listing of my baggage from the carriage driver who brought me here,

a listing of room charges from the Desk Clerk

...AND BOOBAH'S TRANSCRIPT...

FOUR DIFFERENT PAGES WRITTEN BY FOUR DIFFERENT WRITERS IN FOUR DIFFERENT LOCATIONS IN IEST...

AND, YET, ALL FOUR, GREAT CEREBUS...

ARE IN *YOUR* HANDWRITING...

FLIP
FLIP
FLIP

STICK AROUND-- AND TELL *MOST HOLY* IF YOU OBSERVE ANYTHING ELSE.

OF COURSE, GREAT CEREBUS...

NEXT: ANOTHER THING COMING

WITH SEVEN DAYS TO GO UNTIL TARIM DESTROYS THE WORLD, YOU ARE *FINALLY* GIVING HIM ENOUGH GOLD! TO SHOW HIS GRATITUDE, MOST HOLY IS GOING TO TEACH ALL OF YOU A VALUABLE LESSON ABOUT LIFE...

ANOT

THIS MAN WAS ONE OF THE FIRST TO BRING MOST HOLY ALL OF HIS GOLD COINS! TWENTY OF THEM! TEN OF THEM HE USED TO PAY RENT!

FOUR HE USED TO BUY FOOD AND CLOTHES FOR HIS WIFE, HIS SIX CHILDREN AND HIS THREE GRANDCHILDREN

THE OTHER SIX HE HAD INVESTED WISELY TO PROVIDE AN INCOME OF TWENTY COPPER BITS A MONTH!

338

343

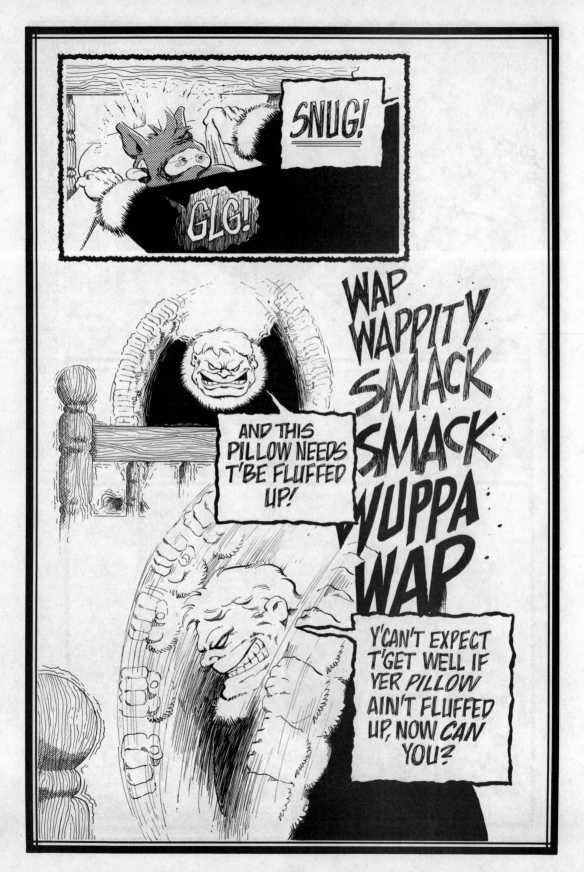

345

346

347

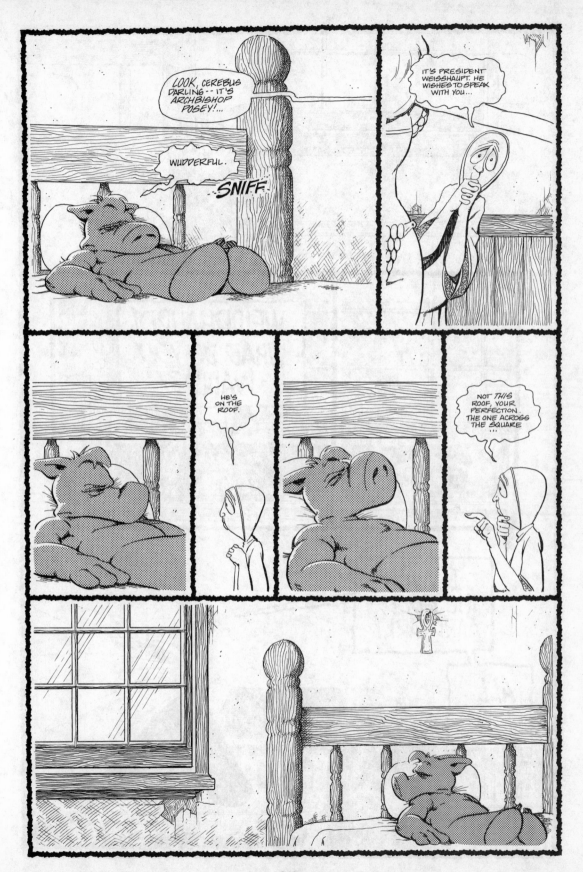

351

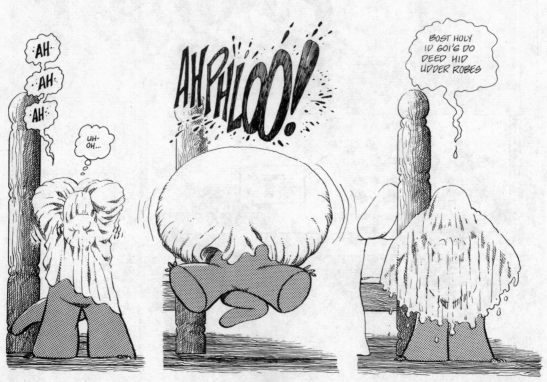

354

356

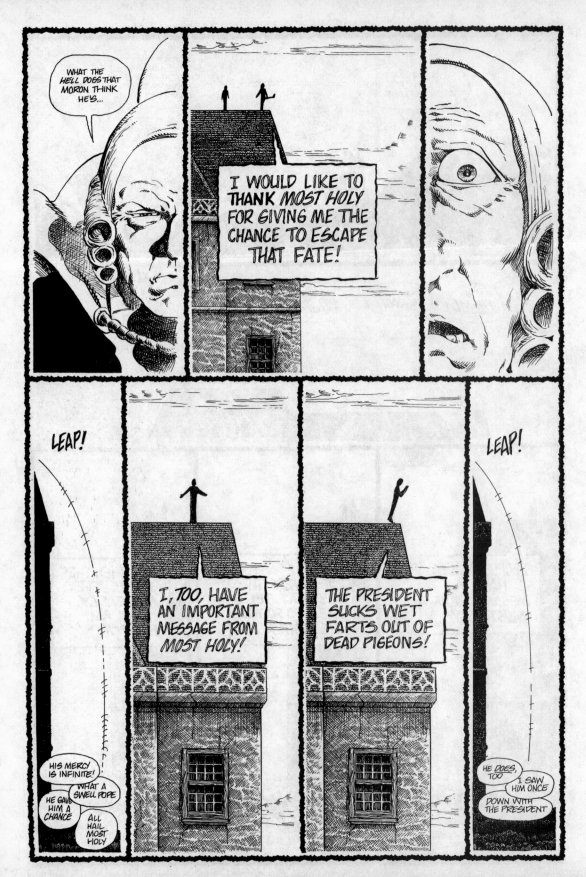

SHOUD BE GOOD FOR AD LEASD ANNUDDER THOUSA'D COIDS

SNIF

BAYBE EBEN BORE

AW, DUTS-- WE SHOUD HAB BROUGHD NA LA'P...

NA LADDER ID AROU'D HERE SUBWHERE...

366

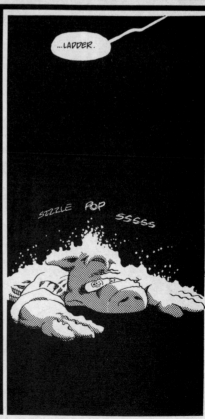

SO... UM...

SO ARE YOU GOING TO MAKE A SPEECH?

BAYBE LADER. RIGHD DOW BOST HOLY HAS A BEDDER IDEA...

BUD FIRSD WE HAB TO FI'D SUB PEBBER...

OUCH!

AND SOME FOOD TO PUT IT ON?

DOE -- DUST PEBBER...

OH.

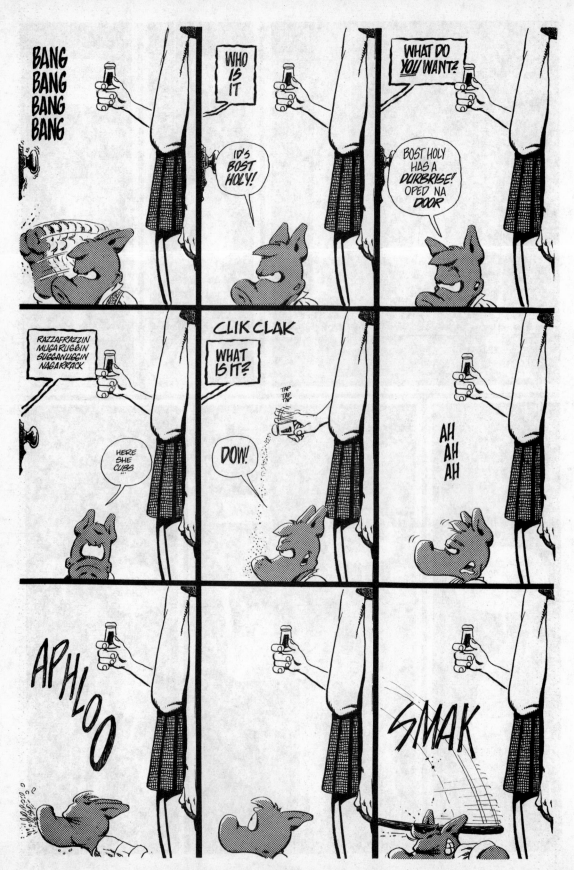

SMACK
SMACKA
WACK
SMACK
SMAT
CRAK
SMAKA
CRAK

UM·· EXCUSE ME... I HAVE SOMETHING TO DO ON THE OTHER SIDE OF THE *HOTEL*...

SLAM

CEREBUS?

ELF?

IT'S HARD FOR ME TO TALK THIS FAR AWAY...

JUST LISTEN

GO DOWN TO THE *BASEMENT* TO THE FAR WALL...

WHERE **ARE** YOU?

IN THE *REGENCY* DOPEY

DOPEY?

PULL THE LITTLE PIECE OF WOOD DOWN AND TO THE RIGHT

A PANEL WILL SLIDE BACK INTO THE WALL

CLIMB THE STAIRS BEHIND THE PANEL ALL THE WAY TO THE TOP...

NEXT: ELF REQUEST

AARDVARK-VANAHEIM PRESENTS

CEREBUS

in

BACKGROUND & TONE
GERHARD

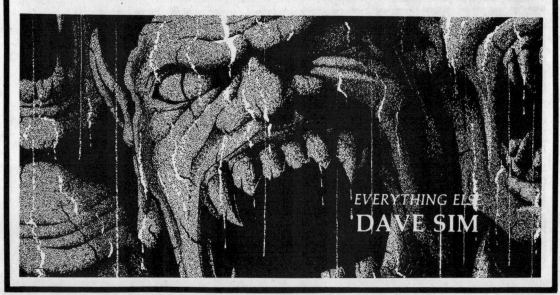

EVERYTHING ELSE
DAVE SIM

375

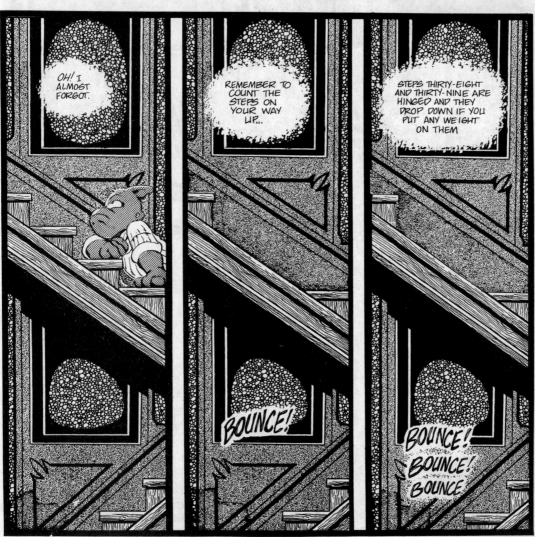

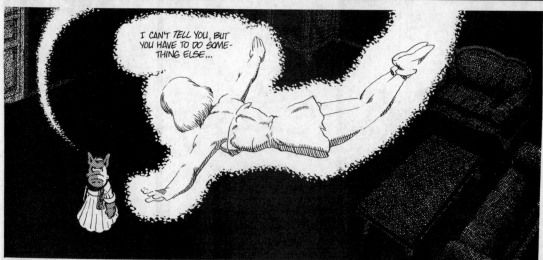

385

386

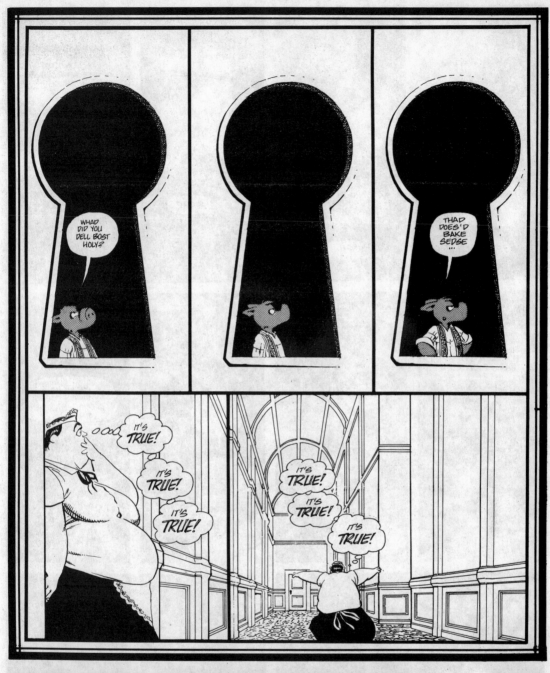

SDARDING WID ALL UB NA DOSDRIL HAIRS?

UH-HUH ...

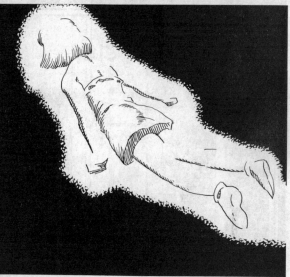

BOST HOLY WILL DUST HAB DO DELL EVERYWOD HE WAD BAKING A *JOGE*... ...

THAT WOULD WORK.

389

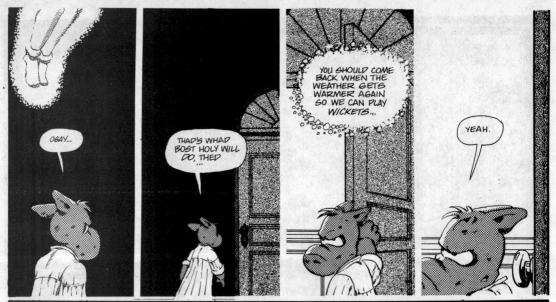

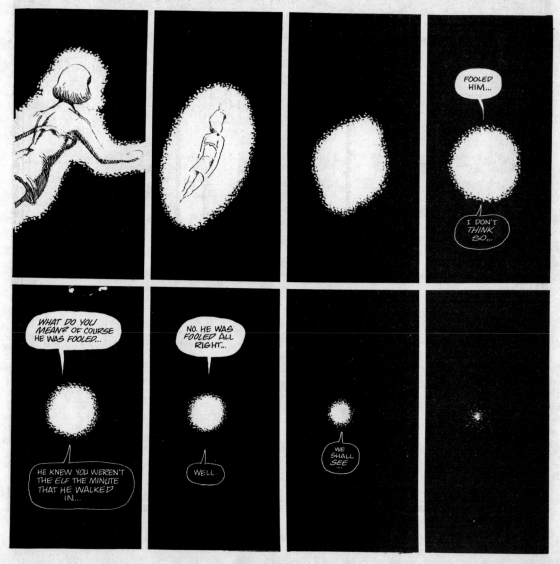

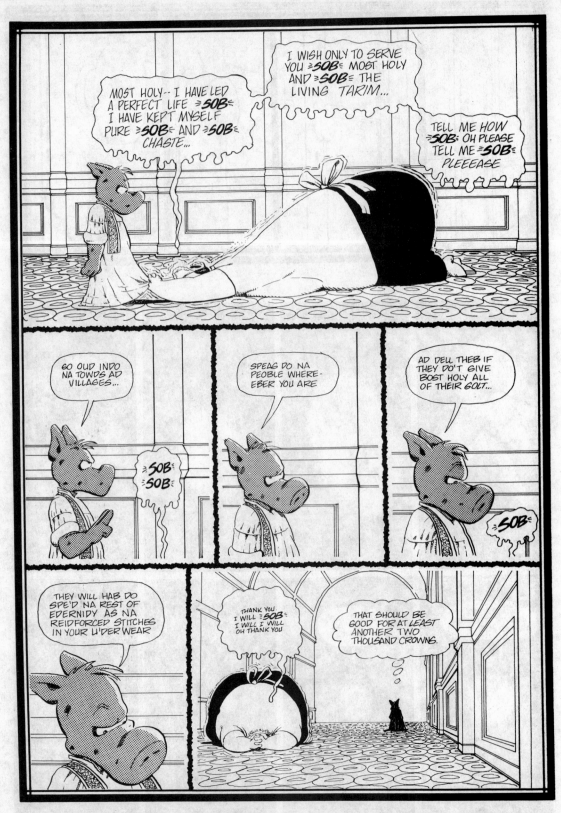

NEXT: **HOVERING BELOW THE FRAY**

HOVERING

BELOW the FRAY

OKAY! SO MOST HOLY CLIMBS UP TO THE *REGENCY* TO GET THE ELF TO ANSWER SOME *QUESTIONS*

AND WHAT DOES MOST HOLY FIND?

AN ELF THAT WOULDN'T FOOL A NEAR-SIGHTED BOREALAN

YOU COULD PRACTICALLY SEE THE *WIRES*

FOR *ONE THING,* MOST HOLY WANTS TO KNOW *WHY* SOMEONE WOULD EVEN *TRY* TO IMPERSONATE THE REGENCY ELF...

AND *SECONDLY,* WHY DID *HE, SHE* OR *IT* TELL MOST HOLY THAT THE WORLD WILL END JUST BECAUSE MOST HOLY HAS *SAID* IT WOULD...

WHY-- BECAUSE IT *WILL,* OF COURSE...

"ALL WILL BE AS GREAT CEREBUS WILLS IT"

THAT IS THE GREAT DREAM

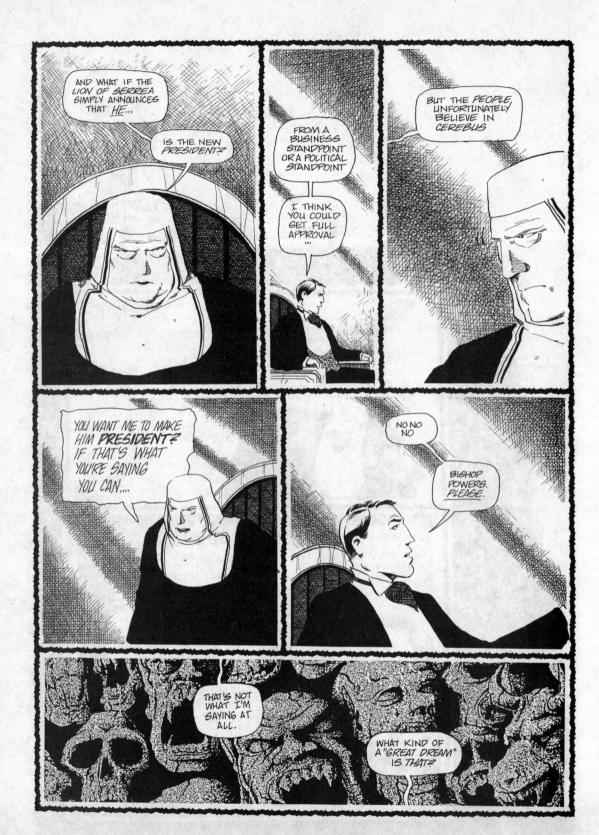

398

400

401

403

404

405

406

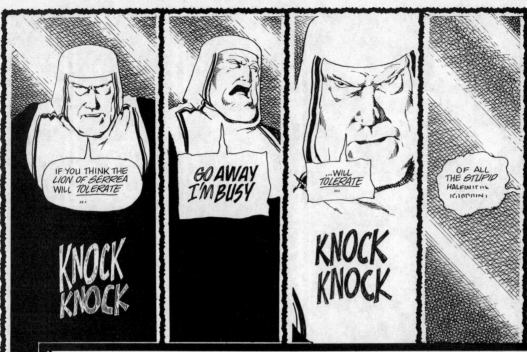

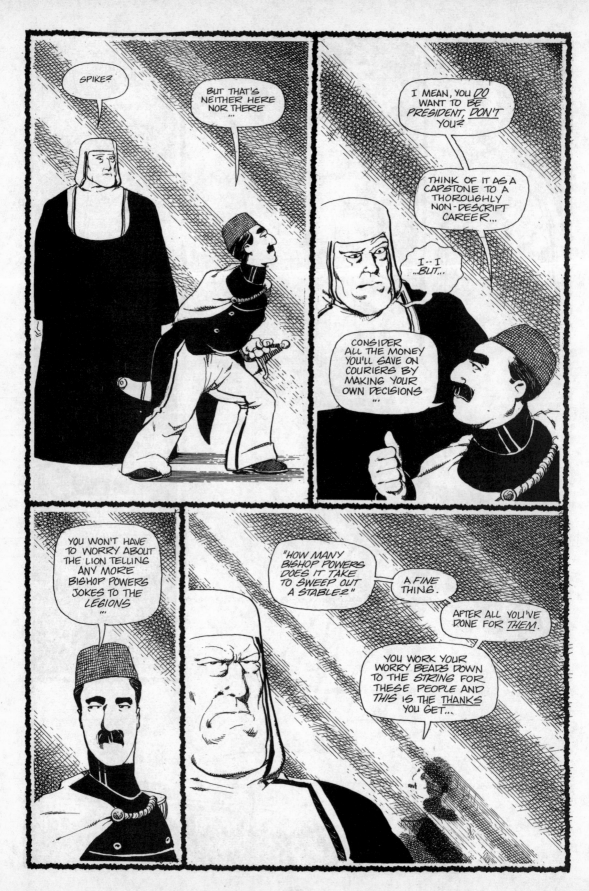

NEXT: YOU ALWAYS FORGET ABOUT THE BEGINNING OF TIME

414

415

416

417

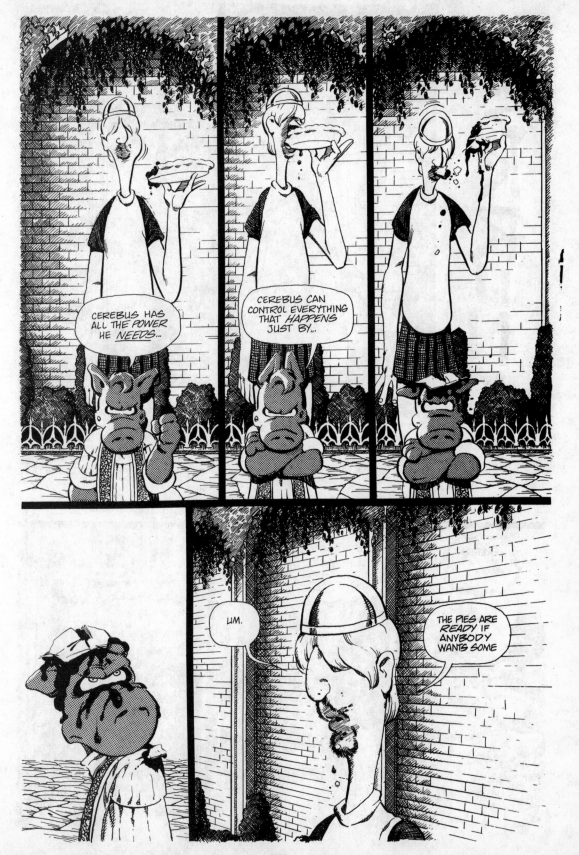

425

430

433

TRIP!

BANG

THUMP

THUMP

BUM

YOU CLUMSY GREAT OAF—IF YOU'VE DROPPED ME GOOD LINENS IN THIS PIG-STY...

436

437

SOPHIA! CEREBUS PICKED UP THE COIN-- THE ONE TARIM STRUCK HIMSELF

FOR A SECOND, MOST HOLY COULDN'T BREATHE....

THEN THERE WERE THESE... THESE RIPPING SOUNDS ALL AROUND MOST HOLY...

AND THEN ALL OF A SUDDEN GOLD COINS STARTED FLYING INTO CEREBUS' HAND...

...AND...

AND.

WHAT ARE YOU DOING?

PACKING.

MOTHER AND I ARE LEAVING...

440

441

445

YO...!

WHAT DO YOU WANT ME TO FORGET *THIS* TIME?

MOST HOLY WANTS YOU TO *FIND SOMEONE* -- AND BRING THEM *HERE*...

SHE'S A *DANCER* ...

...IN THE *LOWER CITY*...

HAS SHE GOT A *NAME?*

JAKA --

ALL IN ONE PIECE -- OR CAN SHE BE BUSTED UP A BIT IF IT BECOMES -- WHATTAYACALL -- NECESSARY?

ALL IN ONE PIECE ...

OKEY-DOKEY ...

452

acquired tastes

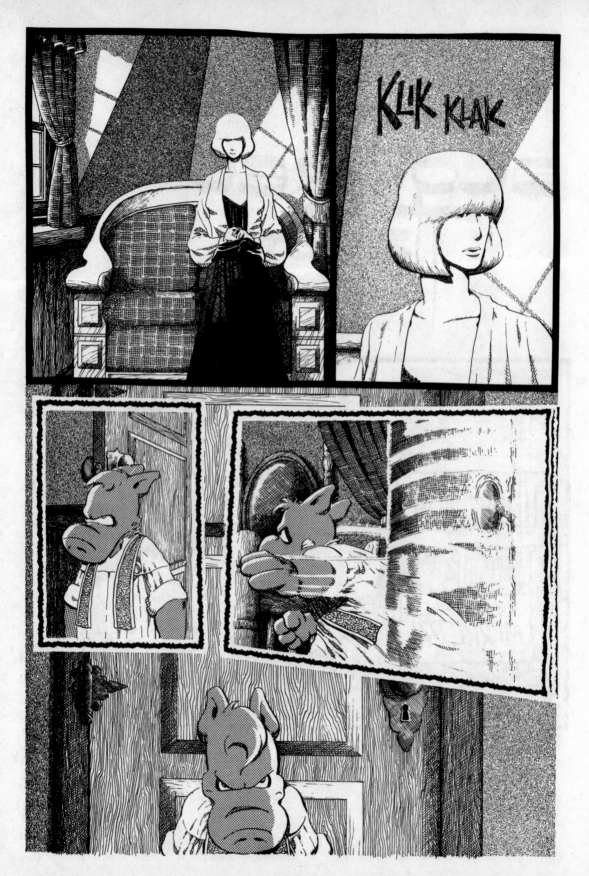

454

455

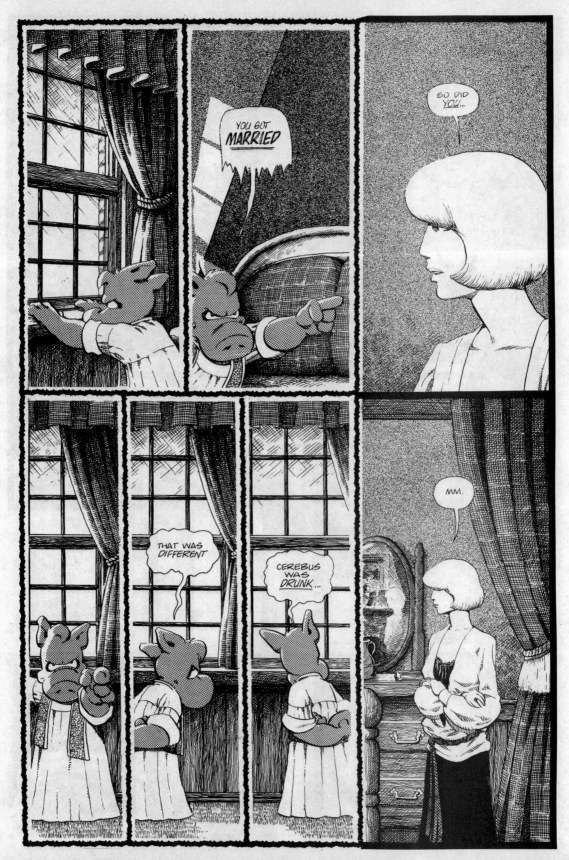

457

458

YOU *SAID* YOU'D WAIT *FOREVER* FOR CEREBUS...

461

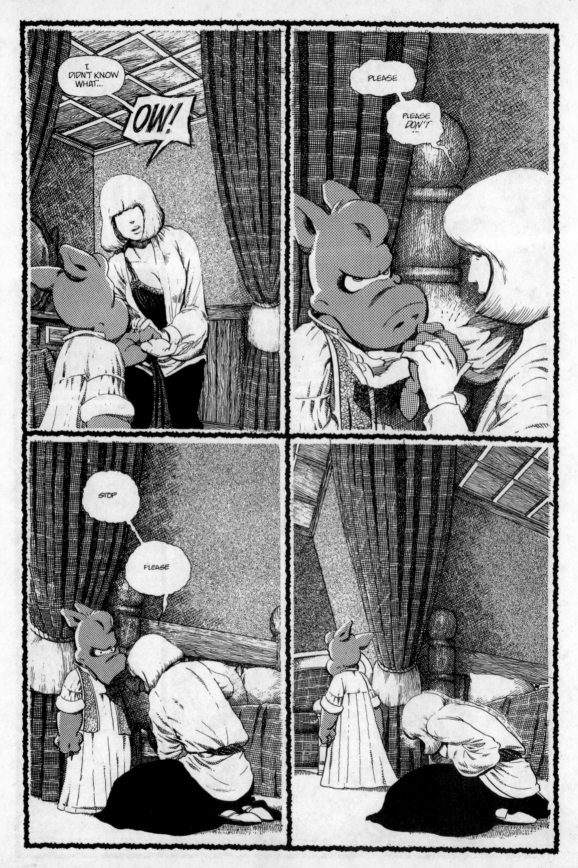

462

465

467

469

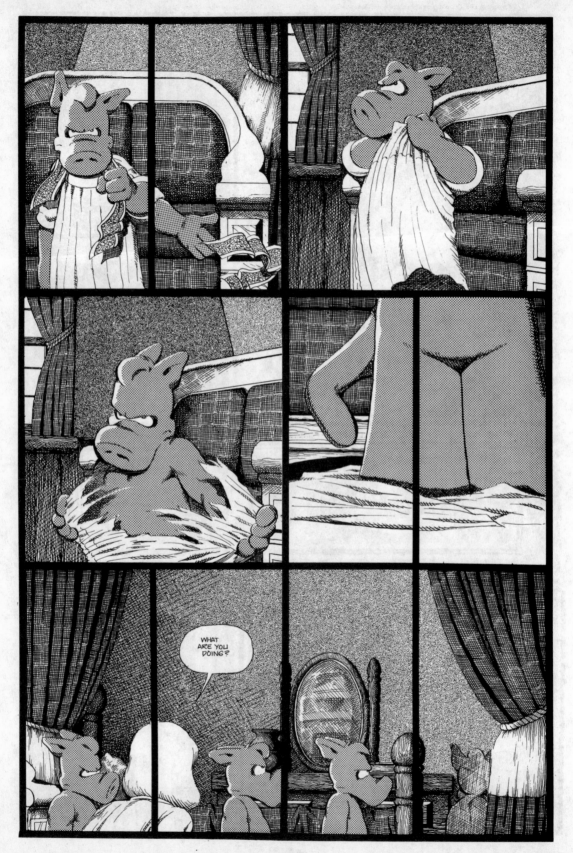

WHAT
ARE YOU
DOING?

470

CEREBUS?

WHAT ARE YOU...

NEXT: TERRIBLE ANALOGIES

TERRIBLE

ANALOGIES

477

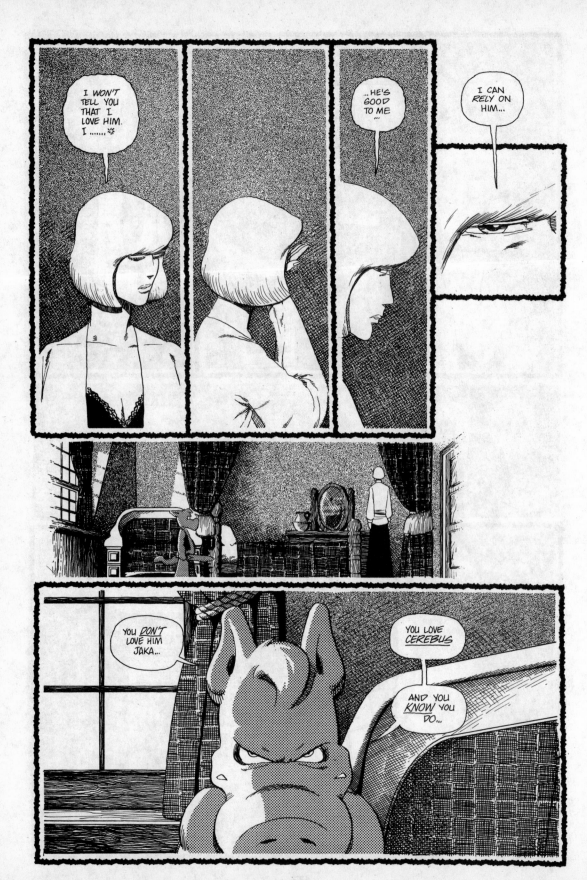

478

479

CLANG KA KLANGANG

486

487

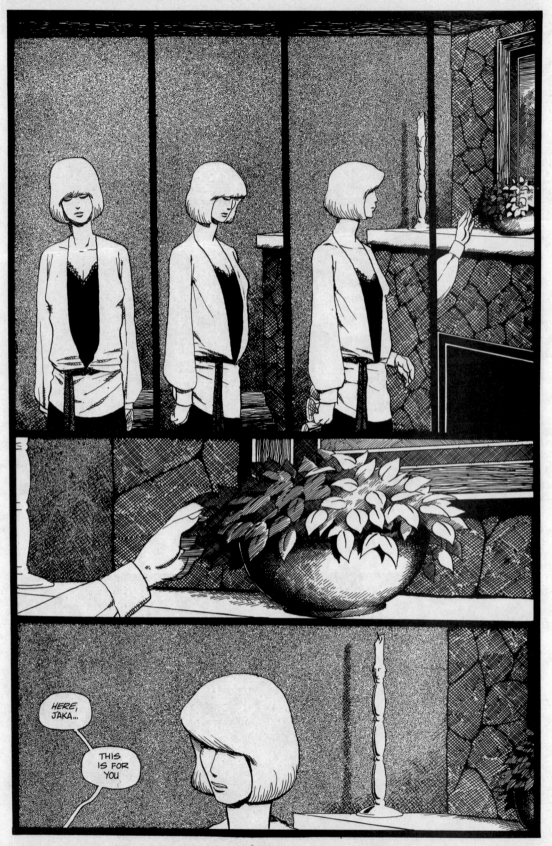

488

489

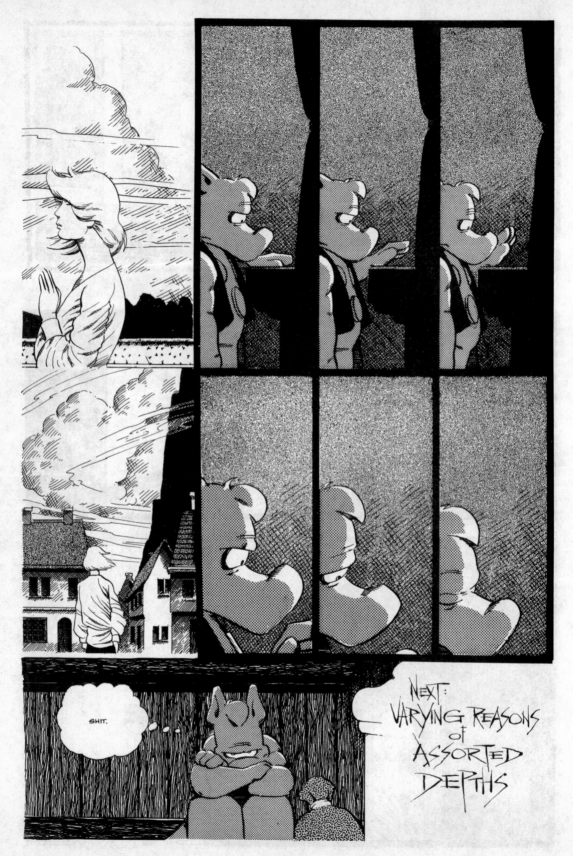

499

YOU HAVE SOMETHING... I DON'T UNDER-STAND IT... I'LL ADMIT THAT.

THE PEASANTS AND LIVESTOCK FLOCK TO YOUR SIDE

CONQUERING THE RED MARCHES WITH SHOVELS... PITCHFORKS...

THEY'RE CENTRAL TO YOUR PLAN, ARE THEY NOT ...

... REPUBLICAN?

THEY'RE SCUM-- THE SAME AS EVERYONE IS SCUM...

CEREBUS COULD JUST AS EASILY HAVE TOLD THEM TO JUMP OFF THE MOUNTAIN

YOU DENY THAT ASTORIA IS STILL PULLING YOUR STRINGS?

CEREBUS HASN'T SEEN ASTORIA SINCE HE RESIGNED AS PRIME MINISTER ...

I DON'T BELIEVE YOU ...

BUT THAT'S NEITHER HERE NOR *THERE* ...

I WANT TO HELP YOU ...

WHEN I'M ... *GONE* ... YOU'LL BE THE ONLY *EXTRAORDINARY* PERSON LEFT IN *ESTARCION*

YOU'RE NOT EXTRAORDINARY AT ALL, WEISSHAUPT ...

YOU'RE AN ORDINARY STUPID, DYING FOOL ...

AND YOU'RE SOMETHING ELSE, WEISSHAUPT ...

YOU'RE A *LOSER*.

UH

501

THIS IT, WEISSHAUPT?

NO...

YOU SURE?

POSITIVE

YOU'RE GOING TO KICK IT WEISSHAUPT

NOT... YET.

FIVE'LL GET YOU TEN

SHUT UP.

YOU'RE...ENJOYING ...THIS, AREN'T YOU?

OF COURSE

CEREBUS WOULDN'T HAVE MISSED IT FOR THE WORLD ...

SO MUCH TO TELL YOU...

SO LITTLE TIME...

YOU MIGHT HAVE TIME FOR A LAST MEAL

IF IT'S A THREE MINUTE EGG

YOU... THINK YOUR POWER IS WITHOUT ...LIMIT...

BUT YOU CAN BE STOPPED

YOU CAN BE STOPPED

YEAH?

BY WHO?

THERE ARE TWO... OTHER AARDVARKS IN ESTARCION ...

504

YOU'RE HALLUCINATING...

OF COURSE I AM...

LIVING WITHOUT HALLUCINATIONS IS LIKE BREATHING WITH ONLY ONE NOSTRIL...

I'M A VISIONARY IN EVERY SENSE OF THE WORD...

YOU CAN TELL, EVEN WITH YOUR LIMITED FACULTIES, THAT I KNOW A GREAT DEAL MORE THAN YOU...

THAT'S WHY YOU CAME...

TO FIND OUT WHAT IS TRUE...

AYE...

NOW THAT YOU MENTION IT, CEREBUS DOES HAVE A QUESTION

AND THAT IS?

THUMP

WHAT'S WRONG WITH YOUR ANKLE?

MY...?

THE FIRST TIME CEREBUS MET YOU -- JUST BEFORE HE WENT INTO YOUR OFFICE...

THE BUG SAID NOT TO STARE AT YOUR ANKLE ...

HOW VERY LIKE 'THE BUG,' AS YOU CALL HIM ...

THE PRESIDENT'S UNCLE ...

HE WAS UNDER STRICT ORDERS TO NOT STARE AT MY UNCLE

MY UNCLE, YOU SEE...

IS SUENTEUS PO...

SO YOU'VE BEEN WONDERING ABOUT THAT ALL THIS TIME HAVE YOU?

NOT REALLY.

CEREBUS IS JUST TRYING TO FILL IN TIME UNTIL YOU *CROAK*...

CHARMING.

TARIM...

TARIM.. THE PAIN ...

IT'S TIME.

YOU WANT TO HURRY IT UP?

CEREBUS HASN'T HAD HIS *DINNER*, YET.

I CAN SEE IT NOW . . .

I CAN SEE

WHERE ARE THE *OTHER* TWO AARDVARKS, WEISSHAUPT?

MOST HOLY . . .

WHERE - ARE - THEY?

510

511

516

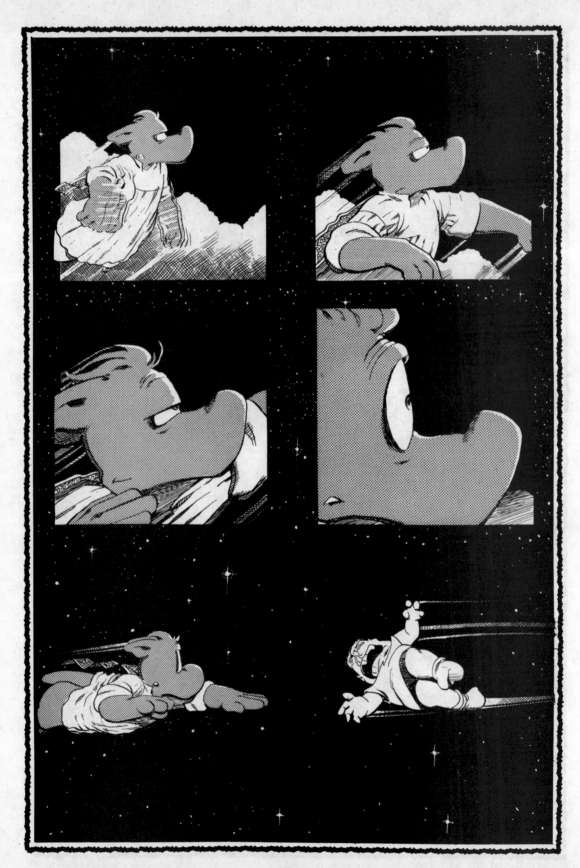

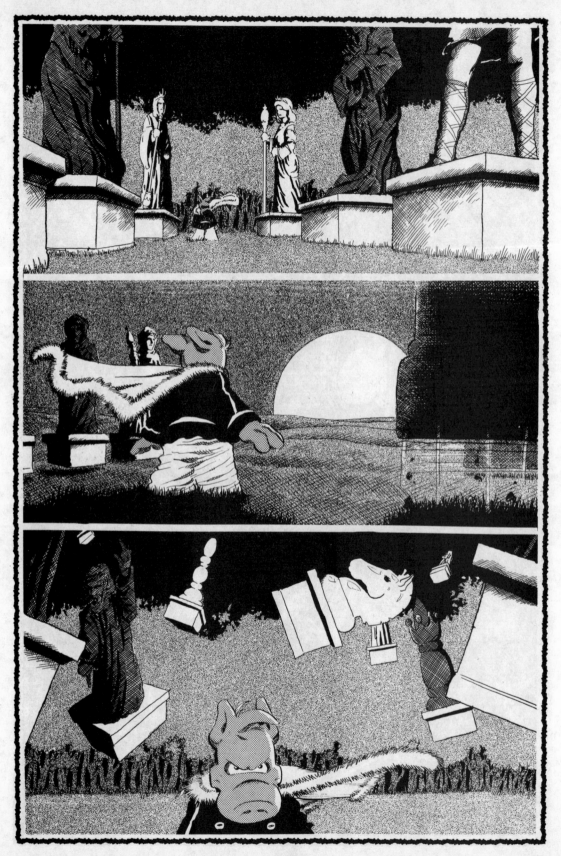

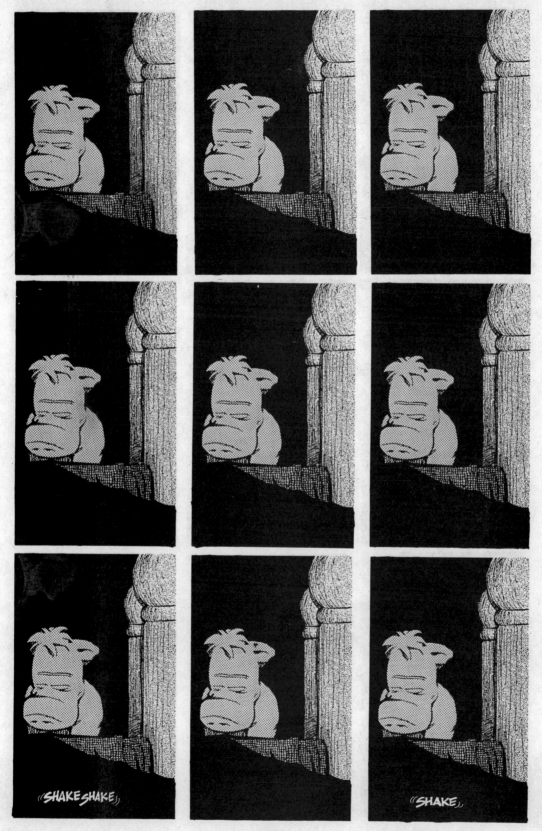

529

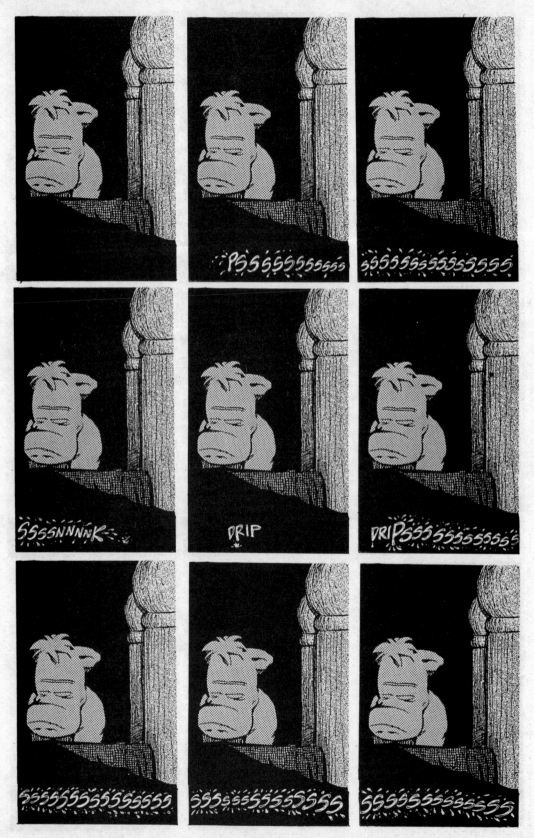

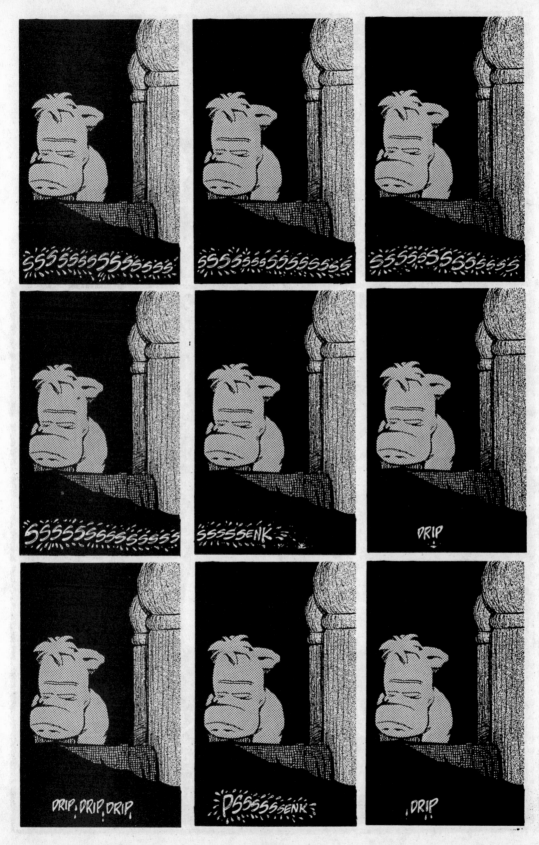

SHAKE

DRIP

NEXT: DREAMING ON an EMPTY BLaDDER

Odd

Transformations
PART TWO

541

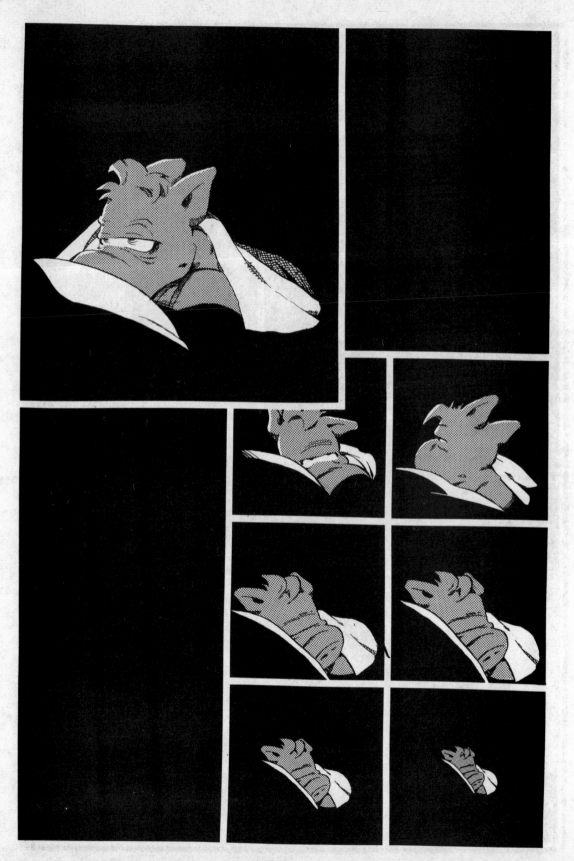

552

554

WHAT ARE YOU DOING?

JUST BECAUSE THE WORLD IS GOING TO END...

DOESN'T MEAN CEREBUS DOESN'T GET HUNGRY...

YOU WERE SAYING?

OH-- UH ≡AHEM≡

FER CENTURIES, THE FOLKS WHO LIVE IN THIS CITY HAD FAITH THET THAR POPE WAS TARIM ON EARTH --THAT HIS CHURCH...

...WAS VANAHEIM ON EARTH... NOW YOU'VE COME HALF-WAY TO THE LOWER CITY... THE FIRST POPE EVER TO DO THAT...

AND YOU'VE TOLD THEM ALL THET EVE'YBODY'S JEST AS WORTHLESS AS THEY WAS AFRAID THEY WAS...

CHIP CHIP CHIP CHIP

TOLD THEM THEY MIGHT AS WELL BE ...

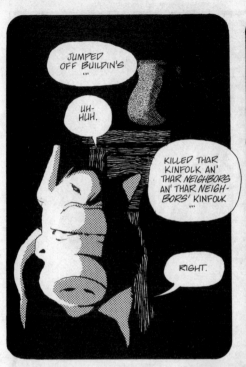

560

564

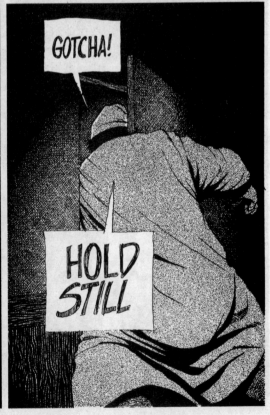

568

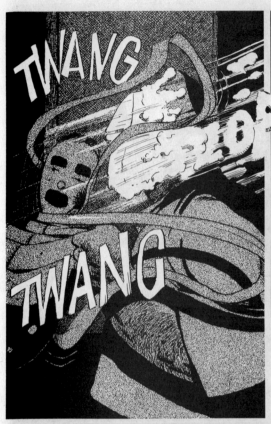

NEXT: MEANWHILE, BACK AT THE STORY-LINE...

WAL, JEST AS A F'RINSTANCE THAR'S TH' WHOLE DANG MOUNTAIN TH' UPPER CITY SETS ON...

Y' PROBABLY AIN'T *NOTICED*, BUT IT'S...

CEREBUS!

I'VE BEEN LOOKING *EVERYWHERE* FOR YOU ...

WOULD YOU...EXCUSE US...?

I'D LIKE TO TALK TO MY *HUSBAND* ...

O' *COURSE!* O' *COURSE!*

IT'S NOT LIKE I HAD ANYTHIN' *IMPORT'NT* T' SAY! ...

I MEAN IT'S *JEST* TH' END O' TH' *WORLD*

CEREBUS?

THERE'S A CLOSE FRIEND OF YOURS *OUTSIDE* AND I THINK HE WANTS TO CHAT...

OH, YEAH?

WHO'S THAT?

HE SAYS HIS NAME IS *TARIM*...

IF HE'S *OUDSIDE*, WHY ARE YOU *TAGING* BOST HOLY *UBSTAIRS*? ...

SO YOU CAN LOOK HIM IN THE EYE ...

LOOG HIB ID NA...?

CEREBUS?

579

581

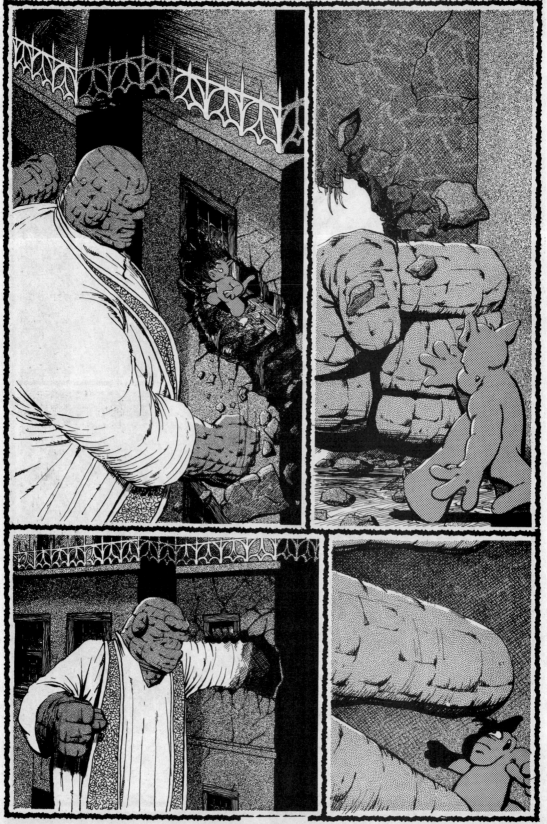

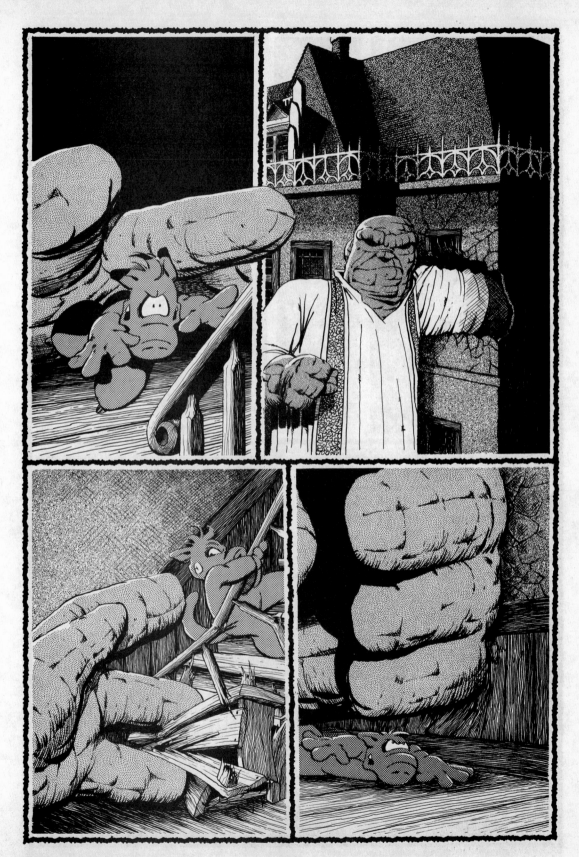

586